THE RISEN

THE RISEN DUST

Poems and stories of passion & resurrection

Rachel Mann

wild goose
publications

www.ionabooks.com

First published 2013
Wild Goose Publications
4th Floor, Savoy House, 140 Sauchiehall Street, Glasgow G2 3DH, UK
www.ionabooks.com
Wild Goose Publications is the publishing division of the Iona Community.
Scottish Charity No. SC003794. Limited Company Reg. No. SC096243.

ISBN 978-1-84952-279-3

Cover image © DTKUTOO- iStock.com

Overseas distribution:
Australia: Willow Connection Pty Ltd, Unit 4A, 3-9 Kenneth Road, Manly Vale, NSW 2093
New Zealand: Pleroma, Higginson Street, Otane 4170, Central Hawkes Bay
Canada: Novalis/Bayard Publishing & Distribution, 10 Lower Spadina Ave., Suite 400, Toronto, Ontario M5V 2Z2

Printed by Bell & Bain, Thornliebank, Glasgow

For my friends –
who've indulged, been amused by
and shared my wild and mercurial passions.

Contents

STATIONS OF THE CROSS

SEVEN LAST WORDS

OTHER STORIES AND POEMS

Blessing

It begins a long way back.
Back before forbidden trees
and grass crushed by anxious feet.
Before a mouth, sore with shaping
new sounds, opened and closed,
failed to speak.

Snow falls, concealing the worn
grain of tracks you have made.
Flake by flake earth recedes,
stepping away, sound throwing off
its weight like seeds.

INTRODUCTION

Does the world need another book which explores and reimagines the passion and resurrection of Jesus Christ? My answer is simultaneously 'no' and 'yes'. 'No' because there is simply no other aspect of Christianity and wider Western cultural life that has been so extensively picked over. Books, art and theology abound. While one doesn't need to be religious in order to be moved by the story of the innocent one who is tortured, put to death and raised to life, perhaps the sheer weight of words gets in the way of our response. I wonder if the time has come to 'shut up' and simply let the story speak again for itself.

Yet, at the same time, such is the importance of the story of Jesus – as cultural phenomenon as much as religious narrative – that I also want more exploration and reimagination rather than less. I say this not simply because I am a person of faith and a priest who – pragmatically – often hungers for resources to use during Passiontide and Easter. I say it as someone who senses that the stories of scapegoating, of power and violence and the persistence of hope contained in the gospel narratives will always be current and significant. Equally, whether we attribute our human sense of alienation to internal or external sources – to an unconscious, to sin, to a god or to social and political ills – the hunger for atonement will always be part of us. The story of Jesus Christ and of those who surrounded him remains a defining narrative of our time.

The Risen Dust is both a practical and a literary book. Its four sections are offered both as resources and as modest literature. I hope they will be used by ministers, congregations and individuals as part of worship and prayer not only during Passiontide and Easter, but at other times when folk reflect on Jesus' story. However, I also hope that, since the book comes at that story with some craft and imagination, *The Risen Dust* may also count as a work of modest literature. That is, that it might open up fresh and sometimes surprising approaches to the passion and resurrection. It is, then, a book which seeks to be sensitive to the gospel records and yet offers critical and literary responses to them. Educated people living in the 21st century can hardly fail to be conscious of how the Bible has been used as a weapon against women, LGBT*[1] folk, those who are seen as poor or mentally ill, minorities and Jewish people. My writing tries to work with the biblical texts, but also is unafraid to write against or extend them. I come from an unashamed feminist and queer perspective and bring a radical instinct to bear on the biblical narrative. Nonetheless, given my eclectic nature, some readers may be surprised by how readily I work with the flow and tone of the biblical text. The opening section, *Voices of Passion and Resurrection*, in particular, offers a way of exploring the passion narrative that attempts to keep my love of radical flourishes to a minimum. It is probably more conservative in its tone than many might wish. Other sections, notably the closing story and poetry section, push the bounds more consistently, introducing modern contexts and both playful and visceral elements.

The title of this book, *The Risen Dust*, is a conscious echo of Genesis 3:19, *'You are dust and to dust you shall return'*, married to the rumour of resurrection contained in the gospel narratives. The abiding power of the story of Jesus for many Christians, including me, is intimately connected to the fact that he was as human as each of us. That is, the one who reveals the way and likeness of God was flesh, bone, blood and dust. The hope contained in the myth of his rising to new life will always be, as far as I can see, terrifying and terrible. For part of me is convinced that the greatest comfort any of us

---

[1] Many people will be now be familiar with the term LGBT signifying Lesbian, Gay, Bi and Trans. As the LGBT 'community' has become more nuanced other terms have been added in: Q (signifying Queer) and I (signifying Intersex). I use the * to signify how complex the queer community has now become.

has is the belief that we are mere dust and this life is all we have; that once it's over, that's it. This may seem the very opposite of the traditional Christian belief in a comforting afterlife and, therefore, thoroughly unchristian. But my hunch is that, as modern Christians, we approach the hope of resurrection too lightly and blithely. There is something terrifying in the notion of resurrection. For while the resurrection may signal the hope of justice and restitution and offer the possibility of transformation for those who experience this life as a vale of tears, it also promises the shattering possibility of being called to account in the face of infinite love. The notion of resurrection is a scandal to the one thing life seemingly teaches us – that once you're dead, that's it. My primitive imagination and human experience can barely glimpse what resurrection might look like. However, I sense the correct response to it is that of the women in St Mark's original gospel ending – a compulsion to run off in terror and amazement in the face of the empty tomb.

VOICES OF PASSION
& RESURRECTION

The following series of monologues represents one way of negotiating Jesus' story of passion and resurrection. By placing those extraordinary events in the voices of characters involved – more or less – in the biblical narrative, I hope to open up fresh ways of responding to those events. They are not as edgy and modern as some might like, nor as conventional as others might wish. They try to balance my own post-modern sensibility with an attempt to place the events in a biblical context. I seek to be faithful to the spirit of the biblical accounts and yet play with them extensively. (The stories in the closing section of this book constitute a more concerted attempt to read biblical stories in radical ways.)

These monologues reflect any number of passions and influences from feminist critique through to Hollywood movies and something as curious as the musical *Jesus Christ Superstar*. Most of all, because these monologues – by their nature – address and break the theatrical 'fourth wall' they reflect my fascination with theatre and drama. It is also worth acknowledging that if the monologues sometimes deliberately read against conventional understandings of the scriptural accounts (e.g. my account of 'A Pharisee' resists typical Christian stereotypes of 1st-century Judaism) they also toy with myths. My picture of Mary Magdalene tries to work with and redeem some of the patriarchal characterisation of her, and the way I voice John, the brother of James, is very much based on the tradition that he lived to a great age. I am also conscious that the inclusion of two consecutive and overlapping monologues in the voice of Peter, at the moment of the Last Supper, might jar. The difference in emphasis reflects the differences between the synoptic gospel accounts and that of the gospel according to John.

The monologues, like all of the work in this book, are also intended as practical resources. Given that 'the Easter Event' is at the very hub of Christian faith and identity, churches and ministers search restlessly for ways to tell the story again. Each monologue can stand alone and may be lifted from the others, though it is also intended as a way of following dimensions of the passion and resurrection through the week and beyond. The sequence begins with the story of the death and resurrection of Lazarus which in John's gospel signals the point at which Jesus' attention is firmly turned towards Jerusalem and the Passover. It ends with an elderly John, the disciple whom Jesus loved, meditating on the events and implications of that defining week.

MARTHA

John 11

I've never suffered fools gladly. Sure, if you're rich or stupid maybe it's easy to relax and kick back. But when you know that if you don't keep it going it's all going to fall apart, it's another matter. Life is too hard and too exhausting to suffer fools.

Maybe that's why it's always been a struggle for me and him to get on.

I'm no Mary and I'm certainly no Lazarus. I'm a grown-up. Because someone has to be. Because my little sister and brother don't want to be. I love them both, but they are like children to me.

Mary … her head full of dreams and fantastic plans; the way I'll send her down to the river to wash clothes and she'll waste half the day trying to catch fish with her hands. She's bright, I know that, but being smart and dreamy doesn't run a house or put food on a table.

And as for Lazarus … he's never been well. He's tried so hard, the poor thing, and if it were down to him nothing would get in his way. But his body just won't have it. He wants to help, but his body lets him down.

So someone has to take charge. Someone has to be the head of the household. That someone is me.

It's hardly surprising that when Jesus came along, he simply dazzled them. Mary sitting there at his feet, Lazarus feeling like he was part of a gang, one of the insiders for once. And I'll give Jesus credit. He loves them both. He's answered their endless questions and shown them a world bigger than I ever could. And Laz was always brighter and happier and healthier when Jesus was around.

It's just never helped that Jesus is more of a dreamer than both of them put together. I'll never forget that time he dared tell me off for asking Mary to come and help me. Can you blame me for being sore? She chose the better part, Jesus said. Yeah, right. He's never had to run a household.

It's his job to do other things, isn't it? Maybe that's why I'm so mad. I don't mean to sound bitter, but if … if he had been here, none of this would have happened. Laz would still be alive. Mary would not have fallen completely apart. And I wouldn't have to be strong for everyone. Again.

Jesus always said he loved Lazarus. He said he'd do anything for him. And I know Jesus and his hangers-on and followers have plans. I know there is a bigger world than us. But why couldn't he have been there for us when we needed him? It's been days since we sent word of Lazarus' death. And we've heard nothing.

Maybe we don't count after all. Maybe that's just how it is with people like Jesus – maybe his plans are bigger than us. Maybe we were wrong about him. Maybe he isn't here for ordinary people after all.

MARY, THE SISTER OF MARTHA

John 11:28-37 & 12:1-8

When I heard he was near I refused to leave the house. I sat in our kitchen staring at the dead hearth, my eyes stinging with tears, my stomach sick.

I left it up to Martha to do the right thing. Martha. The strong one. The grown-up one. Bet she loved that.

But I was too upset, too far gone. Because it was different for me and Lazarus. Because of who he was to us and who we thought we were to him. He was like our older brother or our guide, our friend. He was our rabbi. He was …

We loved him and he said he loved us and would be there for us. And we believed him.

I know he's a busy man, but I thought we were something more to him than a place to say fine things and lay his head. Lazarus was dead and he couldn't even bother to come to the burial. I wouldn't go to him, I told myself. Let him come to me.

It was Martha who made me go. Or maybe it was just the look on her face, so unlike the one she usually wore. Instead of the disapproval, there was something else, something close to hope.

I was not ready to give in though. I was so angry. I wanted to shout and scream and curse. I had all the words laid out in my head. All the words I'd ever need to punish him.

But when I saw him, I crumbled. I fell on my knees and all I could whisper was, 'If you had been here he wouldn't be dead.' I cried then. Or maybe I was crying already. Or just sobbing, because I had nothing left. I was as dry as a handful of dust.

Sometimes you need a shock to see the world straight. Seeing him then was my shock. It was as if the tears had washed mud from my eyes. And I saw a different man. Not the man I loved or a peasant king or a rabbi, but a condemned man. The walking dead. As if he were as dead as Lazarus, yet still upright. I saw the pallor beneath his skin. I saw how lost he looked, as if he was a man who'd been lost at sea for years and ended up in an alien port. I saw his tears.

You know the rest. How he went to the cave and showed us something else. How he terrified us … how he gave us a glimpse of the final day. How everyone tried to explain it away, saying that Laz had just been asleep after all. But I knew different. And Martha did too. We saw a new kingdom that day.

But I can't escape that other man I saw. The dead man, walking an alien shore, the streets of a dark city. He called to me from out of the dark.

Maybe that's why I took that ointment – the most valuable thing we had – and anointed him, touched his feet and wiped him with my hair, not caring if it caused a scandal. I blocked out the disgusted remarks – all the words they used to call me whore and waster.

I thought only of him. Not in the way you might think … But because I understood at last where he was heading … because I saw that there was nothing, no power in heaven or earth, no love – not mine or anyone's – that could stop him. I could not protect him. All any of us could do was get him ready for what was to come.

LAZARUS

John 11:38-44 & 12:9-11

That first day they gathered round as if I were Jesus himself, everyone jostling me, full of curiosity, trying to get the best view. Only the children were cautious, clinging to their mothers' dresses, the adults staring and muttering among themselves … the old men and women drawing in closest, fixing me with fierce eyes, and asking, *What was it like?*

I understand why they all wanted to know, especially the old ones. And all I could say was, *Dark. Dark and cold.* And, in my bewilderment, I looked into their faces and saw mirrored in them my own disappointment and fear.

I know what they wanted, of course. It's what we all want – the story of light and glory, of coming home, of knowing there is a God of comfort beyond this life. But I couldn't give them that. When you've been dead, when you're no longer sure if you're dead or alive, what's the point of avoiding the truth?

Most of them left pretty quickly after that. I didn't move. I just wanted to sit in the sun. To feel as much of the sun as I could on my cold skin. And we spoke, of course, Jesus and I. He said he was sorry that he'd not been there when I died. He said we were all part of something greater. He said that one day we'd both understand. I was shocked by how cold his hands were when he took mine in his and asked forgiveness.

I wonder if I already understand more than him. He's leaving today, he and Peter and the rest. And if you went by their faces you'd think they were going to throw the occupiers out of the country in a single day. You'd think they could never die. You'd think that just because they're good and young they couldn't be broken and nailed up.

I know where they're going. I've been there. And – if I'm honest – I'm still there. And the terrifying thing is that God has never seemed more real. She's there in the dark all right. She's there in the cold. That's why I like to sit in the light and warmth – to get away from her. And it's not that God is malevolent or evil or threatening. That's not what God is like.

It's that she's hurting so much in the dark and ... she's trying to give birth to something new and it hurts so much. It's like she's the pain of the world and she wants to change it. She is the night that is carried through into the dawn.

Maybe Jesus does understand more than I think. I see the excitement on his face – the excitement of a man who's been waiting for the right moment his whole life and takes his chance when it comes. But he's tired too. When you look at his face I'd almost swear he already knows the place I've been.

Or if that's plain stupid, then at least he's smart enough to know that where they're heading is as likely to end in failure as triumph.

One thing I know – Jesus is closer to God than I'll ever be. And if I'm right and God is the pain of the world and wants to change it, if she is most alive in the dark and cold places, that's where he'll be heading too.

PETER (1)

John 12:12-15, Luke 19:28-38, Mark 11:1-11, Matt. 21:1-10

There were days when I hauled in the nets, slick and tricky with fish, when I was damp and glistening with scales and salt, stank of the sea and have felt it. No, seen it: the Glory of God. I don't care if that's blasphemous. As we rowed back to the shore, spent from our work, I felt God's delight.

And what do fancy words like glory and redemption mean except what we feel some days in the rising and the setting of the sun, in the bounty of the sea and the joy of a job well done?

Then he came along and everything we thought we knew was lost.

We must have been mad, given what we did. How we walked away from what we'd always done and known. How our neighbours laughed at us. They called us Jesus' gang of lunatics and fools. And much worse. Feckless and reckless skivers who'd abandoned their lives and homes, forgetting our wives and duties for the sake of a smart-alec preacher. Scroungers and beggars with no self-respect.

I don't expect you to understand, but it was like meeting goodness in the flesh. It was like all those sunrises and good days come all at once. I even told him one time. That he was the One. The Messiah of God. He told me to shut up.

And now this. This walk into the city. This is something else. I might have glimpsed glory before, but this is a new world. To have walked with him all this time – to have been part of all that, the dead raised, the broken made whole, the words taking us closer to God – and finally to arrive. To see the palms, to hear the cheers, to be at a festival at which the nobodies are royalty. To see how they embrace him.

They said we were mad to follow him. They said no one would listen. We were small fry. We were peasants. Power, they said, only listens to power. There is no justice for the likes of us and you can't make a revolution armed only with good will and the foolish and kind.

Well, they were wrong. This carnival is our chance. What can stop us now? This week the world is going to change.

A BYSTANDER

John 12:12-15, Luke 19:28-38, Mark 11:1-11, Matt. 21:1-10

Another year ... another idiot ... Will they never learn?

Year after year they come to Jerusalem at Passover claiming, 'The Kingdom of God has drawn near! God's reign is upon us!' Proclaiming it as if we haven't heard it a thousand times before. And each time the foolish people hope and each time their hope is crushed.

I've lived in this city my whole life and I've seen it all. I've seen them all come and I've seen them go. I've had forty years' worth of fiery zealots, charlatans, dreamers, small-town politicians, even dangerous killers. Forty years' worth of rabble rousers who've said we've got to fight to have our freedom; forty years of the holy ones who've said we've got to find the kingdom in our hearts. Each one pushed forward by their little band of supporters as the One, as the Messiah. As the one who's going to set us all free.

How many times have our expectations been raised and crushed?

Perhaps the time has come to face facts. God has turned his face against us. We are not his chosen people. Or if we are, he is bored with us. Or sick of us and our infighting and self-indulgence.

And this year we have a 'chosen one' from Galilee. Galilee!! I ask you. What good has ever come out of Galilee? A bunch of religious weirdos and fanatics. A den of ignorance and revolution. A lot of yokels whose only conversation concerns the price of fish.

To see him and his supporters yesterday, waving their palm leaves and cheering, shouting out their slogans – well, it was ridiculous. Embarrassing. And the worst of it, their messiah, this Jesus of Nazareth, entered the city riding on a donkey. On a donkey! That'll have the Romans quaking! And when this fool of a preacher oversteps the mark, we'll all have to take the consequences. You mark my words.

I was a dreamer too once. I wanted to change the world. I believed that God would save us. Or if he wouldn't, we'd save ourselves. But I grew up and realised you just have to get on and make the best of the world as you find it, no matter how unfair it seems. You have to put up and shut up. And hide when the spears start raining.

But still this Galilean came and grinned and waved, like the moron he is. Our hero for the day.

Nothing good can come from this.

When will they ever learn?

A RELIGIOUS LEADER

Matt. 26:1-5, Mark 14:1-2, Luke 22:1-2, John 11:45-57

I love my people and I love my God. And let's be clear, I love our great feasts too. Passover – well, who would not be full of joy at Passover? You want to know what a God who saves is like? Look no further than Passover.

But still I should prefer a world without crowds. Crowds are dangerous … irrational. Hard to manage. And now they pour into the city – my people gathering from the furthest reaches of the world. Here for the Feast. It is hard not to marvel. And how could anyone not rejoice? I might prefer a more ordered world, but I'm always thrilled, lifted, by the sight.

Except for that Galilean preacher. Jesus of Nazareth.

He's been an irritant for years, what with his intemperate preaching, the rumours of healings, all the talk of miracles. Stupid Galilean peasants will believe anything. They call him King, Messiah, the Chosen of God. Idiots!

I've met him, of course. He's got authority, I'll grant him that. And a good heart. A truly good heart. And he makes some wonderful points. I once heard him tell this extraordinary story about a Samaritan. I mean, a Samaritan, for heaven's sake.

But he is so naive. He refuses to understand how precarious our people's position is here. We keep our rituals and faith by little more than a thread. He talks of justice and mercy and grace and the Lord's favour. Great. But he seems to think that has something to do with changing things here and now. He does not understand how God's time is different from our own. He does not understand that we will get there. But if he keeps on like he has, he'll spoil the fragile calm that exists between the Romans and us.

And now he's here again. And this time it's a thousand times worse.

Two days ago he enters the city with his entourage of simpletons and clowns waving palm leaves, shouting hosanna. As if he *were* a king. And then he heads to the Temple and practically desecrates the place, overturning tables, spouting nonsense about his Father's House.

The man is a menace. He mocks the people and he mocks us and it's about time he learnt to show his betters some respect. Someone has got to put a stop to this. If we have to act, it is out of love for our people and our God. It is because we need to survive in dangerous times. He is the one who is responsible. He is forcing our hand.

JUDAS

Luke 22:3-6, Mark 14:10-11, Matt. 26:14-16, John 13:21-30

All I ever wanted was to be a good man … to serve God, to help other people. And he gave me my chance.

All my life I've had to put up with people teasing me or pushing me around, just because I was smaller than the other boys. Just because I wasn't always as sharp or as popular as them.

Not everyone can be cool, can they? And sometimes I guess I got into trouble just because I was trying to impress other people. I'd steal things or wind up the Romans a little bit just to get attention.

But Jesus saw me differently. That first time we met he just came up to me and smiled and said, 'Follow me.' And I smiled back, and I think I even laughed and, mad as it sounds, that's what I did. I followed him.

For the first time in my life I've had the confidence to be myself. That's what he does for you – Jesus. He helps you be yourself. And, yeah, I know I've been following him around for three years, but I'm no longer just a member of the crowd. Sometimes in order to be yourself, you have to become a disciple and he's set me free.

All I ever wanted was to be a good man … to serve God and help other people. And through him that's what has happened. I've done more good in the past three years than I ever imagined. We all have. He's helped us become good men and women.

And you know the greatest thing? He's given us hope. When you have nothing and other people look down on you and you spend your whole time being ripped off by those more powerful and wealthier than you, you don't know how incredible that feels.

But, now … now, it's so messed up. It's all got out of hand. Even Jesus is worried. I've seen him at night brooding and praying. He hasn't slept properly for weeks. I've always been his greatest supporter, but things are getting weird.

There are people – even some who've been with us from the start – who want to proclaim him king. You should have seen them when we came into town, the way they were waving the palm branches, shouting, *Hosanna to the King*. People are treating him like a god. People are talking of revolution and of overthrowing the authorities. And that's got to be wrong. Surely he's just a man and not a king. And most definitely not God. That's blasphemy.

To be honest, I don't know. Maybe he is a king. If enough people believe it, you can be anything, right? All I know is I'm scared.

I've heard them, you see – the leaders of the Temple and the Romans too. I've been listening out. They're not going to let this get out of hand. The vultures and the wolves are circling. And Jesus is their chosen lamb.

Maybe you're the kind of person who's happy rushing into a fight. Maybe you're the kind of person who'll throw away their life for a cause. But what if that cause has got out of hand?

You know what I think? We should have stayed away from Jerusalem this year. I think Jesus is losing the plot. I think he's starting to believe what they're saying of him. I've seen it in his eyes. There's no way we're going to get away with this.

Someone's got to make this stop. Don't judge me for what I have to do.

All I've ever wanted was to be a good man. And what I'm going to do is for his sake. And my sake. And for the sake of everyone.

PETER (2)

Matt. 21:12-17, 26:26-35, Mark 14:22-31, Luke 22:31-34, John 13:36-38

Who hasn't been so caught up in a dream you thought it was real? We've all ridden on eagle's wings, lived a life of glory, been heroes and kings in our dreams. And then you wake, and it all retreats like the sea from the shore. And the new day begins and you're nothing again.

Are we waking now?

It was all going so well – the palms and the flowers cast beneath our feet, the smiles on everyone's faces. This was going to be it – our peaceful revolution, our Jerusalem spring. And as we entered the city, like princes supporting our king, we asked, 'What next?'

And as if to prove we weren't ready for the answer he started turning tables over. And then it was all shouting and anger, moneylenders cast out, furious words for priest and peasant alike. I don't know what I'd expected, but it wasn't that. He'd asked us to be fishers of men and women, then he starts tearing things down. He starts saying the Temple has to fall in three days to be built again. Says he has to be lifted up.

I've never doubted him. But, for a moment, I swear he went mad.

And now we've come to this night. A night for food and memories and storytelling. A night to remember our salvation. A night for the meal which shapes us. A night to remind ourselves where we've been, who we are and where we are heading. But it's never been like this.

The words he used were so odd – so close to the old familiar words and yet strange and terrible too. He talked of blood and flesh, of covenants of grace, of grain broken open to set everyone free. Words I didn't understand, but felt. Cold and warm, terrible and comforting, all at the same time.

I wanted to hide, like Moses in the rock when the Holy One passed by. It was like being a kid again; as if a child had been invited into the Holy of Holies and knew the glory of God was going to kill him right then.

But he didn't stop there. He said one of us was about to betray him. And it was like a nightmare then. Like falling into Sheol and discovering the dead could walk and talk and there was nothing you could say to comfort them.

And he was saying my name, though I heard it like an echo – *Peter, before this night is through, you will deny me three times.*

Truth is, I laughed. Those words broke the spell. They were silly and absurd. I told him, heaven save me, that he'd lost it. But when he looked at me, I knew he wasn't messing. The sweat on his forehead, dark as tears of blood in the candlelight, and the worry in his eyes. Like someone who already knows he's dead, but can't yet quite believe it. If I live for a hundred years I won't forget that look. I know he's wrong, but he believed what he said. Just that fact was a knife in my guts – me whom he had named his rock.

And now our meal – our meat and wine and bitter herbs, our sacrifice – is done and he wants to go and pray.

And I am scared. And I want to sleep. Surely everything will be clear, will be a little better, if we all just have a little sleep.

PETER (3)

John 13:1-20

I cannot count the number of stupid things I've done.

How, when I was a kid, not even ten, I stood up in synagogue, when they were still trying to dint some sense into me, and said it was all crap ... except it wasn't that polite. I won't say what I really said. It was just a word I'd heard some of the older boys using, a rude word, a grown-ups' word.

And the old rabbi looked at me, eyes tough as an iron bar, and I thought he was going to whack me. His face went red, then purple, his body shaking, and then … he laughed. He roared like a lion. And he said, yes, maybe I was right, but it was still time to pray. My mum didn't see the funny side. I won't say what she did when she found out.

I always had to be first, had to push further than the rest. I was always the last man standing when the new Shavuot wine started flowing. It was always my job to get the party going. I always had to be the one who hauled the fish ashore. If you believed me, I always caught the biggest fish.

Maybe it was my dad's fault. When I was little he said I should never be afraid. The worst you can be is wrong, he said. Maybe that's why I was never quiet. Maybe that's why I was the gobby one who spoke before his thoughts were sorted.

Was it just because of my dad? Maybe it was because I was the eldest too. Maybe it was because of how he was. He always talked himself up, would tell us how he'd stand up to the bosses or the soldiers who'd move us along. But we all knew it was just bluster. Maybe that's why I felt I must push. That I mustn't be afraid.

Except I was. I always was. I led because I was scared to follow. Because I was scared of being left behind.

And then Jesus came along. No one was much impressed when I started following him. They said, 'Simon, you've lost your head. Only sheep follow, and even the best shepherds are scum.' My father suspected this Jesus was one of the worst. A home-breaker. A wolf in shepherd's clothing. A trouble-maker who was going to break the fragile peace in our homeland, spoil things for everyone's families. I was a husband and father. I had responsibilities. It was not my job to go round upsetting people. It was my job to provide for my family, not to fill people with false hope of being free from oppressors. Good news was other people's job.

But if I was learning to follow, I still had to be the first. I still wanted to be the special one. I was still so empty I'd do anything to feel full.

And sometimes I even got it right. That day I told him he was the Messiah, the chosen of God. In that moment I knew I'd got it right ... only to be shouted at straight away for wanting to protect him from his stupid talk of having to face death. And I'll never forget the boat incident – climbing out of the boat in the middle of the lake – thinking it was because I believed in him, but really because I wanted to show the others what I was made of.

And now, this strange night and the meal we've been sharing our whole lives. This food is the story of us, though he has torn it open ... torn us open with new words about broken bodies and blood outpoured.

But he hasn't stopped there. He might already have turned us into vagabonds for love and justice, but now he wants to wash our feet. He's stood up, tied a towel about himself and wants to be like the lowest servant ... he who is the chosen of God, the one who proclaimed the year of God's favour, who has come to set us free ...

And the others – typical of them – say nothing. They let their jaws go slack like the yokels they are and they take it ... Like sheep following his lead.

Why can't they see it? Why can't they see this is wrong? He's acting like he wants this rubbish job, but I wouldn't give it to someone I despised. If he wants to clean feet he's an idiot – like a person who volunteers to fill in middens and latrines ...

And so I find myself standing up, though it's like watching myself doing it, like it's a dream ...

You will never wash my feet ... I sound hollow to myself, like a piece of dry whittled wood. Untuned. But I hear the passion in my voice and I trust it. I hear the chin-out determination of the little boy I'd been.

You will never wash my feet ... you who are changing the world ... you whose hands can bring life to dead flesh, you who are peace-bringer, lover of the poor and the hopeless.

And in that moment I know I'm right ... he wants to make himself a nobody and it isn't right. Not him. So I stand and I speak and he stares at me … and I see in him the strength and love of that rabbi I'd known as a child.

But unlike that rabbi, he does not laugh. He puts his head to one side and smiles. Like he did that day he called me, that day he'd seen me exactly for what I am. And he says, 'Unless I do this for you, you have no part in me …'

He is not angry. I'm not even sure he's disappointed. In the gentleness of his words, in their simplicity, he understands everything about me … about how proud I am, about who I want him to be … about who I think I should be …

He understands that I want him and me and all of us to be old-fashioned heroes. To be the kind of people who kick the backsides of our oppressors … who are fighters … who lead an army out into a field and kill and maim anyone who stands in our way. I want us to be grown-ups shouting the odds against all-comers in the courts and temples. I want us to be powerful. Lords and kings and princes.

Unless I do this for you, you have no part of me … He just wants me to drop the act … he wants me to see things as they really are. As God sees them. That the world isn't going to be changed by power-mongers and princes, or by those who pretend they've got others' interests at heart, but are really empty and fill themselves up with status and position.

It is by becoming a servant. It is by discovering that God is alive among the nobodies. It is by becoming a child – powerless, treated with contempt, a nobody. It is by becoming a servant of all.

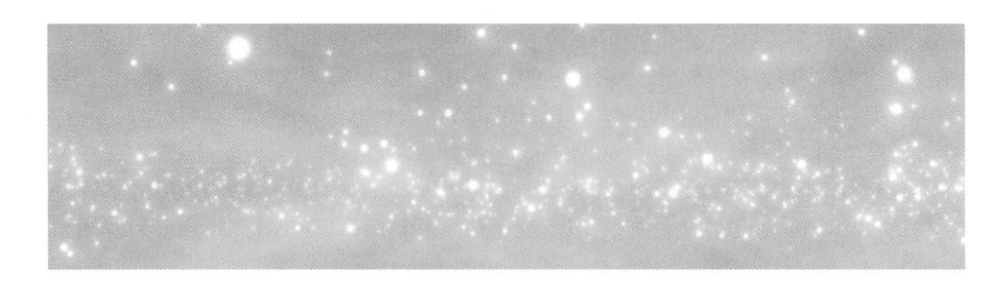

THE ZEALOT

John 18:1-11, Luke 22:47-53, Mark 14:43-52, Matt. 26:47-56

I always wore a sword. I didn't feel dressed unless I carried some form of weapon. Few men did. Jesus understood that. Or at least he never said anything about it.

A lot of us had weapons. We spent a lot of time out in dangerous places. A sword or a club was basic kit. Wild animals or bandits or robbers might attack at any time. You don't know how comforting it is to hold a piece of honed iron in your hand. The knowledge that you can strike back.

When they came for Jesus, it was pure instinct. We'd fallen asleep. Too much food and wine. I reacted like I would have out in the wilderness. Strike first, think later. And part of me still says it was right. It was our last chance to fight back before … well, you know what they did to him. And they were just Temple guards. Thugs. Hired men. We could have hit them hard and saved Jesus. We'd have been out of the city before dawn.

Was I angry with Jesus for what he said and did then? Of course. I'd struck that guard's head, slashed his ear off. There was blood everywhere and we had this one chance to fight. And I was ready. And I know others were too. We had the advantage and the sight of that blood spurred me on.

Put away your swords. I don't know how we did it. Once a sword is in your hand it's so hard to lay it down. It becomes part of your arm, especially if you've been taught to use it properly. It guides you and becomes you.

Perhaps it was a token of our love for him that we stopped. That I let my rage clear. I'd never quite got his man of peace act. His talk of reconciliation. I preferred it when he talked about bringing division. When he talked of bringing a sword rather than peace. When he talked about tearing families apart. When he talked of justice. When he was facing off with the authorities. But I heard his voice then. And I saw what he did for that guard. How he stopped the bleeding.

I saw his stillness and felt his calm. As if of all of us he was the one in control. Like we were children fighting over a toy, getting more and more out of hand. Escalating the violence. He was the stillness at the heart of the storm.

Put away your swords. Those who live by the sword will die by it. At the time they were words. Words said with authority admittedly. But just words. The more I think about them, the more they were a kind of death. They were an end for me, anyway.

I keep looking at that sword, the one I had with me that night. My father's sword and his father's before him. The family sword. The symbol of our capacity to defend ourselves. Of the menfolk's ability to keep our property – our home, our land, our women – safe from thieves and evil. Or at least our ability to put up a fight if trouble came along. To cause trouble if we wanted to, as well.

It's funny. Though I've looked at it, I've not really touched that sword since that night. Was that what I learned through the whole mess that followed? I don't know. There's nothing to be learned from love, except the experience of loving. And it was love that stayed my hand that night. My love for him.

What they did to him when they took him away opened my eyes. I've been violent in my life – who hasn't? – and I've seen violence countless times. But it's different when it's done against someone you love. Against the one who you come to think shows you the very face of love.

And it can go either way. You can plot your revenge. You can make your plans to strike back. Or you can learn, day after day, to walk another way. To see that violence answers no good question.

I look at that sword. My family's sword. And it would be so easy to pick it up. But I choose the difficult way. I choose Jesus' way. If the sword makes me feel safe, I never want to feel safe again.

THE SERVANT WOMAN

Matt. 26:69-75, Mark 14:66-72, Luke 22:54-62, John 18:15-18

I wasn't trying to get him – the big man, the one they called Peter – into trouble. I was in shock too. That's why I blurted it out. Maybe that's why it sounded like an accusation. *You were with Jesus the Galilean, weren't you?*

Looking back I can see why he was so scared when I said it. He'd followed Jesus and his accusers into the courtyard of the high priest. It was dark and there were loads of people. He couldn't have known whether I was a friend or an enemy. And there were plenty of people who would have turned him over if they'd figured out who he was. I wanted him to know he had a friend. But it came out wrong.

I thought he might realise I was on his side from my accent. I'm a Galilean too. But looking back I see that was foolish. It was such a mess out there in the courtyard. A confusion of voices and people. There was no way he would have figured out my intent. I wanted to say, *I'm your friend, Peter. I'm one of you. I'm from Galilee and Jesus has given me hope too.* But all I could do was make my words sound like an accusation.

I'm not sure I've ever seen someone so scared and panicked. It was like looking at a small child who'd just witnessed their parents being dragged off by the soldiers. I knew that look only too well, because it had happened to me.

Peter was there in that courtyard because he loved Jesus, like a child loves a parent. He had to see what they were going to do to Jesus, but every instinct was telling him to run off too. Like an infant all his safety had been taken away when they dragged Jesus off.

When I was a girl the soldiers came for my mum and dad. They didn't give reasons. They didn't have to give reasons. It was only years later that I understood my parents were part of the resistance to the occupation. All I knew for years was that they'd been dragged off. All I knew was what it was like to feel little and powerless. To feel unsafe and a nobody. To feel angry your whole life.

Peter knew that night what it was to be abandoned. I saw it in his face and it terrified him. I could see he'd never quite felt it before. Not that deep. Like a woman or a girl feels most of the time. Maybe he'd always fooled himself that because he was a man he could strike back. That his strength could save him. Maybe that's what made it worse.

I understand why he said, *No I don't know this man,* when I spoke to him. I understand why he said *No* again and again when others asked as well.

But I saw something else. When he denied Jesus I saw a man who was so desperate to say *Yes*, and damn the consequences. And there was a part of me that wanted him to do exactly that. That wanted him to stand there and be proud and unafraid. Or if he was afraid, to stand up for what he knew was right.

We all dream of being something. Of having the courage to stand up for what's right when it counts. I saw something die in that man that night. Something died in me too, if it had ever been alive. I can't see how any of us will ever feel completely alive again.

PILATE

John 18:28-19:16, Luke 23:1-5 & 23:13-25, Mark 15:1-15, Matt. 27:11-26

Life is a simple matter. It's a question of knowing what you can control and what you cannot. Of knowing when to bend and when to be firm. That, I think, was this Jew's mistake.

He's immature. Naive. His politics are too crude. I guess this is what happens when simple folk get ideas. They don't know how to wield them or negotiate. I'm not saying he's stupid – indeed I believe he has more than his share of wit and talent. It's just that without an education these people tend to lash out. Like beasts. They inflame a mob. Like an infant, they lack the character to be able to moderate or compromise. If only they'd pay more attention to their leaders. Leave the thinking to the grown-ups. At least we can do business with them.

I asked a soldier to demonstrate a crucifixion to me once. It was … instructive. I can't remember who the poor soul was whom we crucified. Someone from the dungeons. Does it really matter? I was surprised by how quiet it all was. I mean, not that there was any lack of screaming. There was quite a lot of that. Rather I mean the skill of the executioner was impressive. He got it all done with such little fuss. He knew his tools and task well. There was an understated economy about it.

What I hadn't expected was the intimacy in the act, which I guess reflected my own naivety. On reflection, how could there not be? When two men are drawn together in such proximity, one attaching another to planks of wood, how could it not be intimate? In that moment, one man sees death in the lines and wrinkles of another's face.

And there was something terrific – astonishing even – about witnessing the scene. It made me realise that killing another might be erotic. Exposing. I imagine that's how it feels to enter the arena, to fight like a gladiator does. It was a revelation.

I can't tell you how glad I am that I asked to see that execution close up. It changed me. Changed how I dealt with people like this Jesus and all the bruisers and revolutionaries and wanton holy men who're sent my way. It made me understand that it isn't the fact that we crucify them that matters so much as how. That it is as much about aesthetics as punishment. I think that's made me better in my job. Even though I might not actually hammer in the nails, I strive for my own economy of action. An elegance, a gentleness perhaps.

So when I met this Jesus fellow I was calm. Considered. I like to think he too understood the moment, for he didn't speak. I simply explained what we had to do and why it was important. And there was no snivelling or complaint. I was impressed. If he had any majesty it was in his dignity and control.

I know some men crave theatre and show. And that's what so much of power consists in – the spectacle. That's why we have to crucify them in a public space. But I've always preferred intimacy. That moment when you meet someone face to face and you are yourself. And part of the beauty and power of the moment lies in the fact you've acted with economy. Because you've not made any fuss about an unavoidable act. That's how it was between Jesus and me.

And then we were done. And he was taken away to his fate. And I washed and bathed – like people sometimes do after making love – and I slept and I did not dream.

A PHARISEE

Matt. 27:32-44, Mark 15:21-32, Luke 23:26-38, John 19:17-23

People get saved from the most unexpected things. I saw a man fall down a ravine once – high enough to kill anyone five times over – and get up, dust himself down and walk away. I knew a woman whose ship was sunk on the way to Rome, with all hands lost, except hers. I've seen criminals saved from death and set free for no good reason. But you can't save people from one thing: themselves.

Jesus is one of the most extraordinary people I've ever met. It would be an understatement to say he has the gift of the gab. I've heard him hold a crowd spellbound with little more than a couple of jokes, a few hokey tales and a bit of self-deprecation. I've witnessed him wrong-foot rabbis and teachers with twice his experience. I've seen him embarrass a few people he shouldn't. And I've seen his love and compassion and his fearlessness. He knows you can't love God without loving people.

And, yes, I've heard people say he doesn't get on with the Pharisees. Well that's a joke. There have always been more things in common between us than separate us. How could there not be? Jesus wants to change things. We want to change things. Jesus wants to be faithful. We want to be faithful. And anyway only a fool would say there's only one sort of Pharisee. What a Pharisee is depends on who you talk to. There are people who say Jesus is a Pharisee.

We all want reform. Anyone who wants to be faithful to God does. How else are we going to sort out the mess our political compromises have made? If I were going to be critical of Jesus it would be that he's not radical enough. He talks about paying Caesar what's due to Caesar. Sounds like compromise to me. But I've never doubted his heart and his trust in God.

There are rumours that what's happening here today is the Pharisees' fault – that we've been conspiring against him all along. What do they take us for? Monsters? Just because we've had a few disagreements? If that were the case rabbis would be throwing each other to the dogs every day. Debate and disagreement is what we do. And then we move on. Because it's God whom we all want to serve, rather than the fools who run the nation. But these are troubled times. Lies and mistrust and propaganda abound. People are looking for scapegoats all the time. Like Jesus, we're easy targets.

I've seen people saved from the most extraordinary things. But you can't save people from themselves. That's the only sense I can make of what I've seen today. Because I don't see why it's come to this – a man beaten up and condemned to death for nothing more than his passion for truth and forgiveness.

Jesus is a good man. A fine man. He's not a fanatic. Ultimately, he's holier than some, a bit more eccentric than others and certainly more outrageous than most. But that's no reason for him to be condemned to death and spat on in the street. In the end, he's just one of us.

I wish I had the courage to speak up now. Not because it will save him but because it would be the right thing to do. The Psalmist says to the Lord, *Remember Mount Zion, where you came to dwell. Direct your steps to the perpetual ruins; the enemy has destroyed everything in the sanctuary.* The death of this man, this fine holy man, will cast us further into the ruins. And how are we to rebuild if we do not live for the truth?

You cannot save someone from themselves. I know. Just look at me. I pray that Jesus can forgive me. I hope that God comprehends. That in the ruins we shall find the fragments from which to begin again.

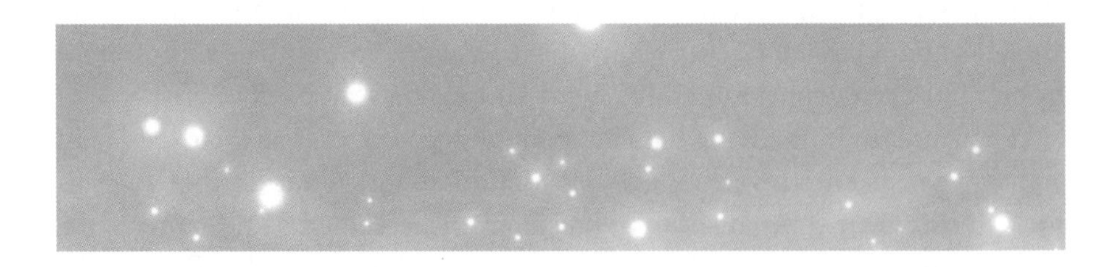

MARY, THE MOTHER OF JESUS

John 19:25-30

Do you know what it's like to hold the most precious thing in the whole world in the palms of your hands?

All those years ago I held him – my firstborn. My miracle. He was so tiny. So tiny I thought, *How can anything so delicate live and breathe and be so hungry?* My baby. My hope. My promise.

Look at him now.

Have you ever held the most precious thing in the whole world in the palm of your hand?

I've been there for him from the beginning. I fed him from my breast, I taught him his first word, I held him when he scraped his knee and cried. I stayed with him even when he said those hurtful words in front of me, 'Who is my mother?'

I'm with him now.

Have you ever held the most precious thing in the whole world in the palm of your hand?

No mother wants to let her child go. Not in her heart of hearts. She wants to keep her babies safe. But even as we hold them, we have to let them go.

I held the most precious thing in the whole world in the palm of my hand ...

He said he was going to save us all ...

And I had to let him go ...

How often have I wanted to hold him, make him safe ...

Before this day is over I will hold him again.

JAMES

Mark 10:35-45, Luke 22:24-30, Matt. 27:32-44, Mark 15:21-32, Luke 23:26-38, John 19:17-23

I blame it on my childhood. And having a brother just a year younger than me. You egg each other on. You want to see who can run the fastest, jump the highest, make the biggest mark.

And then you grow up and it all gets boring. You end up working for your dad in a dull little village where the most exciting thing is seeing who can mend nets the quickest. And your wits start to dull and you're scared you're turning into your dad. I swear John threatened to walk out, to ask dad for his inheritance – Ha! Inheritance! – at least twice a week.

Who wouldn't have taken their chance with Jesus? The look on my dad's face the day John and I left the village! The look of fury and scorn. And behind the wrinkles and weather-beaten skin, the jealousy, and maybe even a bit of admiration.

I am not a man of words. I am – as John, the little git, puts it – as bright as a rusty sword. But I know what I have seen. It's not just the stuff none of us can explain – the healings, the exorcisms and so on. It's not just the way Jesus is fearless, a poor man standing with the poor and loving anyone who doesn't seem to count. I was there that day on the mountain. John and Peter and I saw something. It was like seeing the glory of God. It was like Elijah and Moses were with us.

Jesus calls us the sons of thunder, John and me. It's that childhood thing again. The competition. He gave us back ourselves, our belief. And we can't help it. We egg each other on and want to be first in line for everything – for food, for jobs, for the good news itself. And when you've seen the stuff we have, can you blame us? Jesus is no ordinary bloke. Well, he is and he isn't. I love him because he's one of us. But he's not, as well. It's like being the right-hand man of a king or a prophet. It's like Joshua hanging out with Moses.

It was a bit of a joke really – the way we went up to Jesus and asked to sit on his right hand. We'd pushed each other into it. We just wanted to be involved. We were on the way to Jerusalem and we'd seen the glory on the mountaintop. Now we were going to see his glory in the world. We only said what the others were thinking. We just wanted to be close to the action. We wanted him to know how much we were with him ...

And then the way they looked at us and whispered behind our backs. It was like a shadow descending upon us, a taste of what was to come. We knew we'd annoyed them and they were jealous, Peter sitting there acting all bruised and brooding, as if we'd taken his place.

Even when we entered the city, even on that day of celebration, it wasn't quite the same, as if John and I had tried to load the dice. Especially when everyone was jealous of the way John and Jesus got on already.

Maybe it's taken this day to wake all of us up.

I wanted to sit at his right hand, one of the sons of thunder, but when it all went bad I ran off like the rest. When they arrested Jesus I bottled it and pretended I didn't know him. I'm not sure I'm ever going to handle the shame of that.

But I still love him. I saw what the soldiers did to him in the courtyard. I watched as they dragged him through the streets and when the crowd started shouting *Crucify him!* I shouted too. Because, when it came down to it, I was that afraid of being different, of being spotted as one of his friends.

And there he hangs, broken and despised and bruised. And in my selfishness and stupidity all I can think of is what I asked – to be on his right hand in glory. To share in his work and reign.

What sort of king has a criminal hanging at his right hand?

THE SOLDIER

Matt. 27:32-44, Mark 15:21-32, Luke 23:26-38, John 19:17-23

I hate this place – its dust, its miserably poor people, its stupid little god and these people's bizarre rules and their refusal to be governed.

Most of all, I hate this time of year. The city fills up with pilgrims from all over the Empire, all for a strange festival that no sensible person can understand. It's a nightmare. I'm a soldier, not a crowd-controller. And the worst of it: there's usually some comedian who fancies taking on the might of the Roman Empire, all on his own. Some fool clambers on the Temple steps and starts saying that Israel's got to be free and stirring up the crowd for a riot. And then we have to arrest him and imprison him, kill him even, and the Jews just hate us all the more.

Take this one we've just nailed up. They say he's been fomenting revolution. That he caused a riot in the Temple. They say he claims to be a king or a god or something.

I heard something else. There's a story going round the barracks that he healed a Centurion's daughter up north. I heard that this man doesn't want to destroy the Empire but show us a new kingdom in the heart.

And we're killing him.

I'm sick of it. Sick of this place, sick of the violence I'm asked to commit. When I joined the army I believed in Rome and all she stood for – civilisation, peace, culture. Now I don't know what I believe.

All I know is that when I was about to hammer the nails in he gave me such a look. Like he was sorry for me. Like he was forgiving me.

I'll never forget it if I live a thousand years.

THE WOMAN HEALED OF SEVERE HAEMORRHAGING

Luke 8:40-48, Matt. 27:45-56

Who hasn't seen crosses a hundred times? You see them all over Judea and Galilee. But I never imagined it could happen to him – my saviour, my friend, my king.

I want to shout at those who mock him, and hit them. I want to scream and run away and hide. I don't want to see him like this – naked, hung from nails like an animal. His bruised face. His moaning and weeping.

But I have to stay. He gave me back my life when I'd lost everything. How can I leave him now?

I'll never forget that day he changed my life. I'd been ill for twelve years. I'd bled and bled and could not stop and I was unclean. No one would touch me. No one came near me, not even women, for fear of getting my curse. Mothers singled me out, frightening their children with tales that they'd end up like me if they were bad or faithless. But I thought, *If only I can see him, if only I can reach out and touch even the hem of his robe, I will be free. I'll be healed. No one need know.*

But he knew. He said he felt the power go out of him. I was so scared then. I thought he was going to spit on me. I thought his men would chase me off and call me a whore. But he touched me and held me and told me to go in peace because my faith had made me well.

Jesus showed me the face of God and I've followed him ever since.

I see him on this cross and I see a man who has had everything stolen from him. I want to ask God to have mercy and let him die, but I'm scared all my hope will die with him. I feel like I'm dying too.

Where I once bled from wounds that would not stop, now he bleeds. His wounds will never heal. Like the love he once poured on me, his life pours out on the ground. I know this man shows the face of God. But what kind of God has wounds that never heal?

THE SOLDIER WHO PIERCED JESUS' SIDE

John 19:31-37

I'm not a good man. Never have been.

I've been a soldier for twenty-five years and I've whored and drunk and fought my way all over the Empire. I've seen stuff you can barely dream of: Celts running into battle painted blue; what true darkness looks like in the forests of Germania. I've picked up filthy diseases in Rome.

I'm not a good man. I've done a lot of nasty things. And enjoyed them. I've spent as much time on a charge as I have following orders. Why do you think I ended up here, doing this? Nailing these fanatics up … half of them drunk on their god, the other half just criminals. They say the one we nailed up today, the one in the middle, is a bit of both.

I deserve this job. This isn't a job for a good man … It's funny, when I started I liked to look at them when I hammered the nails in. I liked them to know that it was me who was killing them. That no matter how holy or righteous or tough they thought they were, it was someone as ugly as me taking their life. I wanted them to know that their god wasn't going to protect them. I wanted them to know that the world is ruled by ruthless men and the things we're prepared to do.

I don't know when all that changed. Maybe I just nailed too many of them up. Maybe I got bored.

All I've ever wanted is to feel. Isn't that what everyone wants? I've spent my whole life doing this, that and the other – mostly the other – just because I wanted to feel something. I want to feel like they do – these idiots and fanatics and holy men. But I'm not a good man. So what can I do?

And then there's the thing that keeps me awake at night and nags me when I'm alone. When I'm not showing the world what it's got used to seeing. My secret – that I hate all this. I hate the pain and the screams. I hate looking at their eyes.

I hated that one – the one in the middle – most of all.

The one they call the King of the Jews. He looked at me. Just looked at me, staring. And he knew. I swear he looked past my face and saw what I really am. He knew how much I hate all this. He knew how empty I've become. I almost gouged his eyes out for that.

That's what a bad man would do. And I'm not a good man.

We were told to break their legs. For the sake of the Jews and their festival. Nutters. You know, when you break their legs they can't breathe any more. They can't push themselves up. They drown in their own water and blood.

Sometimes I don't mind breaking their legs. It's like I'm being merciful. Like I'm helping. It makes me feel good. Better. That I can do something kind.

But I didn't want to touch him. Not the one they called the king. I don't know why. It was his eyes. The way he'd seen what I was, but didn't judge. He knew I wasn't good. He saw I was nothing. And he didn't judge.

I was glad when we didn't have to break his legs. But I had to shove the spear in his side. To make sure he really was dead. They'd have killed me if I'd said no. But he was already dead. It was like he was being merciful to me. He gave up his spirit so I didn't have to hurt him any more.

I think he was good, that man. I met him once, that was all. And I was his killer. But he still loved me.

I don't cry. What's the point of tears? But that water that flowed from his side was like all the tears I've never cried pouring out. It was like all the pain I've ever caused flowing out of his side.

When I'm alone tonight, maybe I'll weep. And I'll pray that he – wherever he is – might find it in his heart to forgive me.

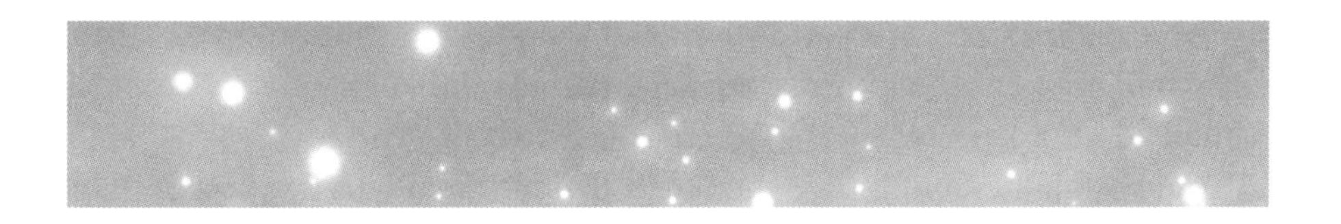

MARY, THE MOTHER OF JAMES THE YOUNGER AND JOSES

Matt. 27:45-56, Mark 15:33-41

Unless you become like little children you cannot enter the kingdom …

I never understood why Jesus said that. I always thought, *What does he know?* He might have been a kid once, but you soon forget. Unless you're a woman and a mother. Then the world never lets you forget.

It sounds so simple, doesn't it? It almost sounds attractive … become like a kid …

Children are so full of life. I remember my boys, little James and his big brother Joses, sticking their noses in everything, buzzing with energy even when we had nothing … being cheeky and climbing trees. That's not so bad, is it?

But that's not what he meant. Not if he's the person I think he is. He's not some mushy sentimental fool. He cares for proper stuff.

What I think he meant was become a nothing, become a nobody. And you don't have to be a woman or a mum to get that, although it helps. I've seen how it works, you see. I know from first hand.

How it's always the kids who pay the price.

How the soldiers and the fanatics make use of kids because they're naive and enthusiastic. I've seen the fanatics using little boys and girls to set traps for the soldiers or make diversions. I've seen soldiers using kids as shields and hurting them to get at us. Both sides are as bad as each other. Both sides use kids for their own ends.

I've seen girls get used and abused and then told to shut up. I was still a girl when my betrothed hit me. And my parents didn't say a word because he had good prospects.

And with James and Joses, when their dad hit them I did my best to fight for them and stand their ground, but how do you fight when everyone says you should just do what you're told? It's a miracle my boys came out whole, though they were scared of their dad till his dying day.

Become like a kid. Jesus might as well have said become like a woman. He might as well have said step into the shadows, lose everything … be despised … be nothing.

I wouldn't be stood here now if it weren't for him. I was at my wits' end. James was heading no place good, into the hands of the fanatics, or worse. But Jesus showed him another path. And me too. He's always treated women well. Has seen us. I'll always love Jesus for that. But I never got his line about becoming like a child. It's like he sets you free, gives you a voice and standing and then talks like we should give it all up. I never got it … till now …

Today they've nailed him up and today I know he understands. Today he is truly one of us; today he is a child. Today he is a woman and a little boy and a little girl.

MARY MAGDALENE (1)

Matt. 27:45-56, Mark 15:33-41

A heat haze, distorting roofs and hard ground and the shape of trees. That's what it was like when he stepped into my life.

Though everything was out of shape back then.

I'd been an ordinary child I think. Though even that seems hazy too now. I played and ran like the other girls. I dreamed of being happy.

I'd had dreams, dreams that made sense to me at least. You see, I'd seen my mum and she was good and kind and lovely, but she was never at ease. Having eight kids to look after didn't help. But she was so clever and smart. Smarter than my dad. But he was the one who made the decisions and would threaten her when she came up with stuff, or showed up his moneymaking schemes for the crap they were.

I'd had dreams. Why couldn't I be someone? Why couldn't I have a life that added up to more than being a wife and a mother and an obedient daughter? I was as sharp as any of the boys in our village – my tongue showed that – but I never got why they should have all the chances.

'Marry her off. She needs to be tamed. Give her to old Ben. He knows how to ride a feisty horse.' That's what the elders said to my dad. Just because I'd been going out alone. Just because I'd been answering the men back. Just because I'd spoken up.

My mum despaired. She argued and reasoned with me. Told me she understood, but how each of us had to learn our part. Had to play it even if it never felt right. Otherwise it would go harder for us. Women could dream, she said, but only at night, when their husbands were asleep. We had to be like birds who sing only in the darkness.

I would not listen of course. And it went as my mum said. I was an embarrassment … an ever-growing embarrassment … the girl no one wanted … the girl no one would marry… the girl who could not learn her place.

They said my mum died of a broken heart – rubbish – but it was what the village said after she dropped down dead when I was barely a young woman. My dad had already gone.

Then the rumours started. That I was possessed. That demons had got hold of my tongue. That I was lost. I laughed of course. But how long before rumours start to stick? I even started acting up just to annoy those who talked about me.

But it's never that simple. Not when you're a woman no one wants. Not when you're a woman. Not when you're an embarrassment, even to the remaining members of your family.

I should have left while I had my chance, but already everything was out of shape. And if people call you mad for long enough and they mock you and throw stones, maybe you do go mad. All I know was that I was alone. And they called me prostitute because I wouldn't give myself to men. And when the men came and tried to take advantage, then my demons became my saviours … it was the only power I had to scare them.

But I was lonely … and never had enough to eat … and people ignored me or shooed me away. Maybe I was possessed. Then he came along.

I thought he was like the others. He came towards me and I thought I knew what he wanted. I knew what men always wanted. I played my game. I acted up … I sought to save myself …

But he was different. He said nothing at first. He just smiled. That half smile I grew to love. That hinted at a sadness to come. And I saw that this man might understand … that though he was a man he was an outsider too.

They say he cast out seven demons. They say he forgave my sins. All he actually said was one word … my name … Mary … and that was enough. He saw me and I saw him and the haze became still. He had spoken to me as if I mattered. He spoke to me as an equal.

I began to live again …

Now I see him dying on a cross. And the haze trembles again.

And when he is dead I shall go to him and bathe him and anoint him and keep his body safe. For I know how lonely it is to be dead and despised. And if I can I shall keep living. And he shall be alive in my struggle for justice and what's right.

MARY MAGDALENE (2)

Mark 16:1-8

The men never understood why the three of us even went there that morning. But since when have men ever understood anything? They want women to be decorative, to cook and look after them, to stay in the shadows so that they're free to play at their stupid schemes. Well, we'd seen what that had come to.

We had our own work to do, Mary, Salome and I. And we did it together, away from the eyes of the men. They might think we were sneaking around, but it's different for them. If you're a woman and you want to act, or want to think, it's safer to do it in the shadows. With friends. With other women who understand. At dawn, when men are still sleeping.

The irony was that because we were just women we could act. We could just go to him. The men were wanted. For once they were the ones who had to hide.

We knew where his body lay and we went to him at dawn. We said it was to anoint him. And that's what we would have done. But really it was to think about what came next. About what lay in store for us, the women. For we weren't like the others, the men who had lives and wives to go back to. We lacked that place to run to.

We thought there might be soldiers. Some kind of guard at least. Someone we would have to charm and distract. We were prepared for that.

We would have hated it, the flirting and the rest. But we needed to get that stone rolled away, so that we might be with him in the dark. So that we might pray and anoint him and think. We thought we would be safe to talk in the dark of that tomb.

But the world is never as you want it. You'd think we'd know that by now, wouldn't you? Being women. When we came to the place where they'd laid him, there was no one and the stone had been rolled away.

I was angry when I saw that. I thought the authorities had done it. Had stolen his body. I never imagined they would stoop that low. Then I thought, *Oh God, what if it's one of the disciples who's done it. What if they've gone mad and stolen Jesus' body.*

Part of me just wanted to leave. To walk off in defeat. I saw the fear and the anger in the others' eyes too. But it was like we couldn't stop. We had to look inside. We had to see what was there. Or wasn't. There was something that made us step forward into the tomb despite ourselves.

I don't know to this day if it was a man or a woman who sat there. Whoever they were they were dressed in white. But sometimes when I try and think about it they seemed clothed in flames. It's like I can't get the events in order.

What I do remember is how my body felt. I remember my insides burning. How my breathing became quicker and quicker and I almost felt drunk. I remember the words of the strange person who sat there. But that wasn't really what was astonishing and, yes, terrible. My body felt wild and new, like I'd been born that moment. And there was something else. A thought maybe, though that word isn't strong enough. It became clear to me that I didn't belong to anyone or anything. That I was free. That although I was a woman I did not need to be afraid of the day. That God was alive and so were we.

And it was tremendous and frightening.

And we stared at each other – Mary, Salome and me. And I saw that they felt it too. And we laughed. And we ran.

CLEOPAS

Luke 24:13-35

We were just glad to get away. I was sick of the hubbub, the near hysteria, in the city. Maybe I just needed to grieve. Or to begin to grieve. To let the shocks of the previous days begin to sink in.

Perhaps, then, it wasn't surprising that I was a little hostile to the stranger who joined us on the road to Emmaus. I know that's appalling. Roads can be dangerous places. It's always wiser to travel in groups. And it was a failure of hospitality.

But I wanted the comfort of silence. And the comfort of being with someone I knew. Who understood the confusion. Who understood from the inside what it was like to lose the best person we'd ever known. Who'd also been there in the midst of the women's rumours that he was not dead at all. Who'd seen men and women losing their heads over rumours. Just the two of us walking the road, left to our thoughts and grief.

I'm not good with new people at the best of times, but I was as cold with him as I dared be. I nodded and kept my eyes down and we walked off into the afternoon.

I will give him his due, this stranger. He was no gabbler. If the silence was awkward, at least he let it be silence. And as we walked further away from the city, I began to breathe again. I've always found God in the open spaces. God, as they say, is spacious. And God so often speaks in the silence.

But though I felt a weight begin to lift, I'd also have been happy if none of us had spoken for the whole journey. We must have looked so odd to him as we walked – the way we kept our eyes on the path, the way we walked almost in step, like soldiers do, finding comfort in the rhythm. Perhaps it was inevitable that he would speak.

What's the matter? It was such a simple question, an outrageous one for a complete stranger to ask. But sometimes it's easier to unburden yourself to someone you don't know and will never see again. So out it tumbled, the whole astonishing story, my disbelief that this man had no clue about what might be on our hearts.

If God often speaks in the silence, sometimes she speaks into it too. She spoke then, through this man. His words were simple, like those of Jesus had been. They were words that began to break open the scriptures for us. That began to make sense of what we had seen in the last few months and in the days just passed. He talked of sacrifice and grace, of the way God is like a pregnant woman and there must be birth pangs. Of how we were all being born anew.

When we arrived at Emmaus we begged him to stay with us. It was nearly night and we were hungry for more. I wanted to laugh at my change of heart – glad for this stranger's presence and words, when earlier I'd resented his every step. So he joined us in the house and sat down to break bread.

We break bread every day. When he took the loaf in his hands, grey and dull in the half-light, there was no miracle. It was and always was mere bread. But when he broke it, for us it crackled and roared. He might have been tearing apart the world. Or a life. A life lived and given for others. And we saw. And we saw him. And it was an end. And it was the beginning of all things.

THOMAS

John 20:19-29

John got it all wrong of course. But, then, since when can you trust a writer?

Here's how he set it down: Jesus had been crucified and we were all scared and lost and huddling away from the crowds. That much I'll give him. We were as low as we'd ever been. It was like losing your best friend and your brother and maybe your mum and your dad all in one go. Some of us might as well have been dead ourselves. A couple couldn't even speak.

And all I wanted to do was get out. Be busy. Do something. Anything to stop the moping around and worrying and indecision. Anything not to have to think.

And someone needed to do something anyway. We had no food. No one knew anything. Someone had to find out what was going on out there in the city. And that's one thing they never got about me. Yes, I need to think. I need to see. Maybe I need to question. But I'm not just the doubter. I have to check stuff out. I want to think for myself.

I was gone for no time at all. The sun had barely moved in the sky. For all that, I might have been away ten years.

I returned to uproar. It was as if the possessed who roam the streets begging for bread had come into the house.

The first thing I said was *Shut up!* The authorities were on the lookout for us. That much I'd gleaned from the streets. These idiots were risking arrest, torture and death. No wonder I was furious. My frightened voice, dragging up all the authority I had, stopped them dead. And then we got down to it.

John likes to pretend that they all spoke as one, but it was harder, stranger … more human … than that. There was the crowd who swore it was him. Who swore that all the things we'd ever known – that the dead stayed dead, that flesh and blood can't walk through walls, that a man getting beaten senseless then tortured and killed on a cross might not be enough to finish him off – were wrong. All this lot wanted to do was run out in the street and rejoice, like drunks taking their party out where it wasn't wanted. They were like children.

And then there were the silent ones. Those who didn't know what to say. Who refused to trust their friends or their eyes. They just sat there dumbfounded. As if what they'd witnessed had deprived them of the power of speech.

And of course there were a couple of sensible ones, who said they'd felt it or seen it too, but who said it was too soon … they needed to think … to work it out …

To which I uttered my immortal line … *Unless I see him face to face and put my fingers in the holes of his hands and his side I shall not believe* … except I didn't – well not exactly. John makes me sound like some street performer playing a role. The set-up man for the punch line … the one who tempts fate.

I just wanted some clarity. I wanted to get to the bottom of things. If I said the line at all it was almost as a kind of joke, as something to change the crazy mood. Something to give us space to think. I needed to shock them out of the madness. I know some of those present laughed, but others thought I was a fool, that I was practically a blasphemer. At least it shut them up for a bit.

And all I could think was that if Jesus had been there he would have understood me.

Because the one thing he always got about me was that I had to figure stuff out, that I had to use my mind. He knew I'd studied a bit. I'd travelled and heard the words of philosophers, Jew and gentile. I'd never been like most of the rest. They wanted it simple. They lapped up his talk of trusting the Lord, of following the Way, of sowing seeds and reaping the harvest. Yokels.

But I always wanted more. And Jesus understood. He always said that though in the end we have to find our own way to be faithful to God, there are many roads to get there. Love God with everything – including your mind …

My mistake was always to think that mind was enough. To imagine that wise words and sayings were the thing. That really that was how we should see him: as another one in a long line of teachers. Part of me will always see him that way… as the man of words who could wow a crowd … who could cause laughter and tears and outrage and fury. But that was not the man I met when he returned.

I touched his skin you know, or he touched me … or that was what it was like …

You might think they never let me off the hook after that, the others. That life became a thousand *I told you sos*. I heard someone give that as an explanation for why I left for another part of the world … that I couldn't hack the innuendo. But it was never like that.

The others were kind. They saw that in my doubt, my questioning and my hunger for the truth I'd received a fearful gift. How can I put it? Love, in its simplest, most passionate form, always tears us apart. And meeting Jesus again was the simplest love – the love of recognition, which bypasses all the tricks of clever men and women. God tore apart everything I thought I knew and understood. And when I finally walked off to tell the world about it, it was because God was making me anew. And I knew that – despite everything pointing another way – this God, this Jesus, was creating the world anew too.

PETER (4)

John 21:1-19

The blueness of the sky, blue as grapes on the vine, blue as veins under the skin and the cedars bending towards the waters. The water of the lake as cold as a dead body. Those are the things I remember most clearly now.

His face I can barely remember. It was so unlike him and yet who else could it have been?

We had gone back to what we knew, at least for one night – casting nets and hauling, as much for comfort's sake as anything else. Not expecting, not even wanting, to catch anything. We just wanted to get the muscles working again, to do something routine. Anything to stop the thinking and the doubting and the fear.

We thought it was all over, you see. Sure, we'd been changed and we knew we couldn't go back, but we were lost too. What else do you have when it's all fallen apart, except the things you've always known?

Smoke drifted across the water as dawn came, its scent rich and lovely, as if rosemary had been thrown on the flames. Like the fires on that Passover night.

I was the first to understand. After all, who knew we were here? No one fished in this lonely place. Who could it be but him?

I dived in, swam like someone trying to save a drowning child, the water making my limbs numb, the fire on the shore my guide. I stumbled onto the sand, shook salt from my hair and saw him.

There was no flash of light, no cloud around him, like that day on the mountaintop. There was just a man, cooking fish in the embers. Just a man, as defenceless and ordinary as me. In peasant's clothes. He sat by the fire and gestured for me to sit down.

And then the others came and sat and pulled at the flakes of fish, tasted the sea, all of us eating like people who hadn't had a proper meal for weeks.

We had not known how empty we'd become. All of us eating, except him. He just sat back and smiled.

I cried then. Because I'd let him down and failed him in his hour of need. And as we stared at him, the scales falling from our eyes, we were talking, all at once. Till one by one we fell silent and let him speak.

I only remember him saying one thing. *Peter … feed my sheep*. Again and again.

And I tried to reassure him. Said I would do it … Three times he asked and three times I tried to make him understand, pleaded with him.

But I'm not sure he believed me. And why should he, given what I'd done that night when we'd all fallen away? I'm not sure I quite believed myself.

Now I see that was the best place to start. Given what I've had to do since, given where I've been. For on that shore, I had no idea what was really being asked of me.

Yet for all that, since that day, it's been a simple life. Feeding sheep indeed! Except that that breaks down a thousand ways … I've learned that standing alongside the hated and the lost and vulnerable always does. To make an idiot of yourself in public for the sake of love and goodness … to be an idiot in the face of the powerful and the torturers.

I see now that he always knew it was going to end this way for me, that they'd do to me what they did to him. That I'd be humiliated and broken. Except they'd be the stupid ones who could not see the glory.

I've tried to follow him, and now, at the end, I pray that I have.

Though what I'd give to see him with me now. I feel him in the nails in my hands and feet … but to see him as I did that blue morning, the fire guiding me. Stumbling through the waters with the energy of a young man, as only a young man can, seeing the sun rising ahead of me.

Soon, perhaps, soon. Soon there may be another shore.

JOHN

John 21:20-25

Did it do any good? Did it accomplish anything? That's what I ask myself now.

An old man's questions, I guess. The questions of the last one who could say, *Yes, I was there*. Who can close their eyes and still see it.

They're all gone now. Peter and Andrew … Thomas … Mary and the women … and my brother James. I don't care what pious folk say about how, on that Last Day, the Day of Resurrection, we'll all be gathered together. There isn't a day when I don't miss my brother, pillock that he was. The older I get the more I wish he was here still. To share the things only we knew. To get the chance to tell him, just once, that he was the best of me.

All things must pass. I know that better than most. And I'm amazed at the community we're becoming. But there's no one like him and that group of friends and scoundrels and fools we were back then. They were my feast.

The older I get, the less I know. You know, there's this rumour I won't die until Jesus returns. And now I am old, as old as anyone should ever be, and some of the community are excited. It can't be long, they say … Fools. God doesn't make bargains, like a farmer selling her goods. She makes relationships.

Maybe that's why I'm full of doubts, despite everything I've witnessed, despite the community we've become.

When I was young I wanted everything and I wanted it right now. I wanted to sit on Jesus' right hand, for heaven's sake, and judge the world. Now I can't even picture what Jesus looked like.

Except in one respect. I remember that day and him on the cross. I remember how young we all were, even Jesus' mother, though to me then she seemed old. And when he said to me, *Here is your mother*, I thought, *He's saying something else, something more.* That out of all the vileness of that day, something more had to come. New ways of going on. That's why I know God makes relationships. She is the one in and between all of us.

And later, when we met Jesus again on that shore, I thought, *Surely it can't be long. It can't be long before all things shall be well and justice will be done and there will be a new heaven and earth and grace will flow like rivers.* And I thought of all the destitute and hungry people, the prisoners of power and money and the broken and lost. And how we were them too. And how surely soon it was all going to be all right.

But God is not to be gainsaid. God has her time. And that's why I doubt. Because as old as I am there will always be part of me that wants everything now. That doesn't want what God is really offering us – a part in her creation, in making relationships and bringing change that lasts and moves as slowly as an old man. I don't want to be part of the labour pains. The God I want is a miracle-maker, not the broken one on a cross giving birth to us.

As I face my end, I face my beginning. And all I want to say, again and again, is that I was there. That I too stood on that shore in Galilee when he called us. That I too believed and followed and believe still. That I was there and he was in the world.

And he is in the world still. And one day the dawn will come.

STATIONS OF THE CROSS

The use of the Stations of the Cross as a devotional practice goes at least as far back as the Middle Ages. For many, it is especially connected with St Francis of Assisi and the Franciscans. Whatever the precise origin of the *Via Crucis*, it is true that the emergence of the Stations was tied to the desire of pilgrims to walk the way of Jesus in Jerusalem. In a culture that was mostly non-literate, the visual and physical dimensions of walking the way of Christ hardly need explaining.

For so-called Protestant churches the use of the Stations has commonly been treated with some suspicion. This reflects a number of factors. The brave new world signalled by the era known as the Reformation was often conceived as the triumph of the Word of God over superstition and ignorance. And the Stations – as visual representations of Jesus' final walk to the cross and beyond – are a curious mixture of biblical accounts (whether that be Station One in which Christ is condemned or Station Eleven, The Crucifixion) and tradition (for example, Station Six, in which Veronica famously wipes Christ's face and his image is embedded in the cloth). As such the Stations can cause anxiety in those who consider faithfulness to the biblical text a sign of holiness. Equally, they are typically grounded in visual response and artistic representation. One suspects that some ministers and congregations have been anxious about eyes being ravished by wanton art.

We now live in an age where the visual has reasserted its place in church culture. Many individuals and congregations are attentive to the dynamic relationship between the visual and the written and have rediscovered the power of the Stations. It has been encouraging to see how use of the Stations has broken out of Roman Catholic and Anglo-Catholic confines in recent years.

The following fifteen poems have been inspired by two sources: firstly, my own emotional and devotional responses to using the Stations over many years and, secondly, a new set of painted Stations created by the Manchester artist Rob Floyd for Manchester Cathedral's Lent 2014 exhibition. Digital versions of Rob's paintings can be found on his website *www.robfloyd.co.uk*. The poetry itself reflects my fascination with the lyric form and my interest in a language grounded in nature, fecundity and the intimate. Alas, my gifts – despite my best efforts – are too limited to escape the shadow of my major influences, including Michael Symmons Roberts, Sharon Olds and Jo Shapcott. In particular, poem six, *Veronica*, has been strongly influenced by the structure of Susan Wicks' poem *Knot*. And it was a privilege to have been mentored by Michael in the early stages of my residency at Manchester Cathedral.

While my poems are partly responses to Rob's classical approach to the Stations, they are also offered as poems in their own right. They may be read privately or publicly without visual art. They may be read as a sequence or individually. You might wish to read them alongside the prayers for the Stations written by Ruth Burgess for *Eggs and Ashes* (Glasgow: Wild Goose 2004) or many other sets of prayers. Some will question the inclusion of a Fifteenth Station – the Resurrection or Empty Tomb – since it was not part of the classical Stations of the Cross. In recent times, ending the Stations in resurrection has become commonplace enough to justify including a poem about it. For those less confident about the structure of the Stations here is a brief guide:

- Jesus is condemned to death
- Jesus receives or carries the cross
- Jesus falls the first time
- Jesus meets his mother
- Simon of Cyrene helps Jesus to carry the cross
- Veronica wipes the face of Jesus
- Jesus falls the second time
- Jesus meets the women of Jerusalem
- Jesus falls the third time
- Jesus' clothes are taken away
- Crucifixion: Jesus is nailed to the cross

- Jesus dies on the cross
- Jesus is taken down from the cross (Deposition or Pietà)
- Jesus is laid in the tomb
- Jesus is raised from the dead – the Empty Tomb

Most of all, these poems seek to hold in tension the individual voices and perspectives represented – from Pilate in 'Condemned' through to Mary Magdalene in 'Angels' – and the sense that we are all involved in this story. At the heart of the *Via Crucis* is the profound notion that we are all participants in Jesus' story – as audience, as witnesses and as persecutors.

CONDEMNED

We grow towards what we want.

So the corn breaks earth and stone
to seed for the sun, fields of lavender flow,
moving as women do, loose as a gown.

I reach for somewhere safe
to search back through the layers of a dream,
digging and sifting to another time,
an early time, when men and women
were tried out by gods, first took fire
and iron, shaped the world to their schemes,
back to that imagined first day. A place
where a man might study his hands,
know, at a glance, they are clean.

That it should come to this:
a mob, a man, a judgement. Death or freedom.
The water, at least, is cool, a bowl wide enough
to scrub my fingers, a pool in which I might drown.

TAKING THE CROSS

Who teaches the tree its seasons?
To wait in its bones in winter,
to bleed, weep and bud,
tell the story in rings and girth,
the seed the store of all things.
Who can teach him now?

Not for him the feel of the plough cutting furrows
into the palms of his hands, the taste of snow
on a thirsty tongue, how his face too might finally
sag with all the stories he's ever told.

He is the bee stumbling with its pollen,
the swallow dancing in the fowler's net.
He is the branch breaking in the storm,
he is the way ahead.

FIRST TIME

A child's tumble, a cut knee, a pratfall,
the body's original *I say I say I say*.
Surely, that's all.

And if it were more?
The sow learns her loveliness
nuzzling roots in the damp,

the thrush in the first note of the song.
How often we don't know
what we've become until we start.

His face is getting lost,
like wood blurred from polish and use,
his fingers curled dried leaves.

The panic, as he pushes
at the brittle earth,
how he might scatter easily as dust.

JESUS MEETS HIS MOTHER

It's the crowd in her head which kicks her now,
words awkward as elbows, *man, boy, rabbi, brother, son*,
all the faces he ever wore, *angry, fearsome, fearful, loving, mad*,
back to his childhood, and the shock of weight
when she took him in her arms; back to that first night,
and her groan when the sac of afterbirth escaped her warmth,
back before it all began.

Watching this day from that night,
wanting to take water and bathe him,
as she did then, washing away the muck and blood,
the stuff of her that clung to his skin,
until he was as clear as a stream,
tying off that stem on which he'd flowered,
each other free at last.

She would take him back, of course,
if it would do any good; let her belly swell,
return him to sea and salt and murky dreams,
but he would not go. He is a child of earth now,
cut and bruised, holding the weight of a world
as if it were a beam.

SIMON OF CYRENE

All I wanted was to lift you up
and walk away.

But you grew small, curled down
into my hand, nestling
like a mouse preparing for winter.

How easy it would have been
to finish it there, to crush you,
to save everyone the trouble.

Or to run, carry you off,
find somewhere dark to sleep,
to heal as we dreamed.

But no. We walked
as they commanded us,
you growing tall again,

the look on your face
as we reached the hill,
furious, as if to say,

why didn't you take
your chance?

VERONICA

Let me do for you what they do
for the dead; now, while you still breathe,
your face, simple as a lamb's, pleading.

Let me wash you into shape,
prepare you to be seen, sew back
the seams of broken skin, touch you
with linen and balm;

Or wrap you tight in cotton and herbs,
hide you from your task, seal you
where you can't be found.

Later, when you are dead,
we shall cut the threads,
open the cloth with the delicacy
of silk; lifting off that other you,
the one you carry now,
leaving you clean, your new self.

SECOND TIME

Perhaps he is already done,
his hands and limbs hardening, discovering
the thick, cool stiffness of the dead;
the pulsing code unravelling, soon to spoil
in the pit where they'll throw him,
beating off the dogs with sticks,
and the rush back home to grey bread,
barks echoing in the night.

And if we were kind we'd bring
marvellous girls to bathe his wounds,
garlands and flowers to aid his sleep;
we'd offer him *that* at least, then leave him
to his dreams.

But that is for later, we say,
like a secret deployed when it aids
us best. We know the time for angels,
for soothing balms, a bed on which to rest.

And if we leave him it is because we know
he still has far to go, has centuries yet to meet us.
It is his task to walk them alone.

WOMEN OF JERUSALEM

It was not how you think:
crowds pressing, dust rising,
salt on tongue and face.

More like we had forgotten
how to dance. We who had moved
and twirled to his lead, toe to toe,
the scent of bread and oil on his hands.
We who had made new things,
had worked warm leaven through broken grain.

Is this how it will be?
Our eyes open, or closed,
or held away, like people
at the edge of a sea;
seeing ourselves cast back,
distorted and wavering,
ripples in the dawn.

THIRD TIME

If he were a lamb, half dead, half born,
head hanging dumbly from the birth canal
we'd give him this at least:

quick hands, snapped spine, the mother too,
her slick wool washed, fingers brushed
along the nape of her neck.

But we are unsure what is best,
the body the only way to the soul, we say,
perhaps this is his plan:

to map his own secret history
of what it takes to cure a world;
so we busy ourselves,

hide like children
frightened by shadows,
a familiar face, in the night.

STRIPPED

So many things it could never be:

A robe for a prince, fruit of a thousand moths,
Spun for months, delicate as a conscience

Or a gown for prayer, dark with sweat,
O god of gods, save us from locusts and the blood!

It is just the story of him

Stained with talk of lost sons, a dusty road,
The net which threw forth a lifetime's tales

It is his walking and sleeping, the breaking of bread,
The thread which stitched together a kingdom

And it is all he has left
To keep him safe

CRUCIFIXION

Later we talked of orchards,
of blossom and bud, a human vine
trained by iron, fruit for the dark.

But then I thought only of song,
of melodies fragile as ribs,
of how a monster might hammer music
from a stockpile of bones.

This instrument on a hill
whistled harmonies we could not stand,
as if the dead had been raised
and sang half-remembered psalms.

We left quickly, as mourners do,
hungry for home and warmth,
dust blackening in the rain,

notes beating on the roofs,
the world's heart untuned,
a cold percussion, drowned lives.

JESUS DIES ON THE CROSS

wishing he could nestle now
in the crook of his mother's arm,
the firstborn, the *wonder*, light as bread,
the pearl unexpectedly found

or further back, a sea-being,
smoke-eyed, a creature of mirrors,
darting in shadows, till the trap is sprung,
the net raised high, cast on a beach
to slap and dance, the business quickly done

but he has become the last of his tribe,
deaf to the secrets of words only he knows,
gabbling alone, mouth open, no song

PIETÀ

If you were asleep
it would be easy to say
the things you've never known.

How old age grows round
the throat like a vine,
how it tightens every day.

You'd tell me otherwise.
About ghosts that rise in the desert,
the way grain breaks open and dies,
begins again in the ground. How we
are all born and grow into the dark.

But you have always
been sure of the shape of the land,
touched her curves as a boy
holds a girl, her secrets given up
at the clap of your hands; snapping
open the eyes of the blind
with spit and soil, kicking crowds up
behind you.

If I knew the trick I'd crumble earth, rub it in.
And you blinking awake, I'd stare you down,
tell you the news, *I told you so.*
How you'd smile and look away, walking off
as if there was somewhere still left to find.

ENTOMBMENT

Look at us. Three figures
posed like actors figuring out how to play
grief. One kneeling by the corpse, face pushed
down, another reaching out,
offering a mother's hand,
the man standing apart, arm pressed
across his chest as if to keep his heart in.

But it is too soon for us to know
how to act. Too soon to carry the dead
within us, to walk away, seal the stone.
We are just learning to set him down,
finding out what is safe, like parents
with a newborn.

Can we begin again?
We who have watched our faces
gather into folds, become rutted fields,
who have scattered grains and not seen
them rise.

We might have been here for years,
growing slowly into the dark,
waiting for this one hour of light.
We might have been here for all time.

THE ANGELS

One look was enough
to tell they were already
treating it like home,
her smile restful, a lover's glance,
him, hand in the air,
showing off the place,
a face so smug it would
be a pleasure to punch.

I had come to the deep cold
room of want expecting
to offer aloes and myrrh,
my own salts to cure the air.

They offered me a trick of light –
Look, see where he is not,
search the linen if you must –
but I held the wild kick of hope
deep inside, like a child
struggling in my womb.

I gave them my back,
shielding the gift – my smile –
and ran.

SEVEN LAST WORDS

The Seven Last Words or sayings of Jesus from the cross have, unsurprisingly, become central to church traditions and liturgies for Good Friday. Not all of the seven sayings are contained in each of the four canonical gospels. The sayings may be laid out as follows:

- Luke 23:34: Father, forgive them, for they do not know what they are doing.
- Luke 23:43: Truly, I tell you, today you will be with me in paradise.
- John 19:26-27: Woman, here is your son. Here is your mother.
- Matthew 27:46: My God, my God, why have you forsaken me? (See also Mark 15:34)
- John 19:28: I am thirsty.
- John 19:30: It is finished.
- Luke 23:46: Father, into your hands I commend my spirit.

Given the fundamental significance of Jesus both to the emerging Christian community in the early years following his death and to the developed church, it is hardly surprising that his final words have been the subject of profound liturgical and theological interest. The extent to which these sayings are historically accurate is moot and is not of great concern to what follows. I have sought to take the 'Seven Last Words' and bring a wider context and life to them. I have made them the subject of various responses from characters who, on the gospel accounts, might reasonably be supposed to have been there. As with the earlier monologues, there is both artistic and theological licence and the speakers in a very clear way break 'the fourth wall'. Attentive readers will also note there are eight monologues. Rather than reflect a particular interest in Jesus' statement of forsakenness, it reflects inspiration to write on that subject from several angles.

FATHER, FORGIVE THEM, FOR THEY DO NOT KNOW WHAT THEY ARE DOING

Of all the things I've heard one of them say, that was the strangest.

For if there's one thing we know, it's our job. And we know it because of them. Because they give us so much practice.

It's like they can't help themselves. And don't get me wrong. I reckon that if we were occupied too, we'd do the same. But still, it breaks my heart: Time after time they think they can take us on and we prove them wrong. It always goes the same way.

So one or other of them gets up and starts going on about *god this* and *god that* – about how their god is a god of justice or sacrifice or hope – and then the rabble get stirred up and the idiots get threatening. And then we have to act, before it gets out of hand. So we arrest the ringleaders and string them up. It's rough justice, but it's the only way to keep the peace in a place like this.

The worst of it is they get us all wrong. We're not here because we hate them. We're not even here to convert them to our ways. Haven't we let them keep their god and their rituals? We've poured money into their economy. Their problem is small-mindedness. They don't see the big picture. They think it's all about them.

If we gave into them, who next? If we let them go their own way, if we let them welter in their own tribal disputes, then the whole damn world might come tumbling down. And don't get me wrong. In some ways I admire these people. I admire their tenacity. I admire their courage.

But to claim we don't know what we're doing. It's ridiculous. I've been here five years now. This is practically my home. I have a local girl. I even know their language. And I'm good at my job. They hand me the extremists – the rebels and the fanatics and the criminals – and my boys march them up the hill, nail them to the wood and lift them up. Job done.

And I like to think I get it done quickly. Efficiently. With the least fuss. With the least cruelty. So don't tell me we don't know what we're doing.

Sometimes I want to show these young men and women the fruits of their actions. I've dreamt of taking them down to the pit and showing them what happens to the stupid. Down to the pit where we throw their dead bodies. Where we deny them their rituals and laws. Maybe then they'd learn. Maybe then they'd realise we know exactly what we're doing.

We're not cruel. We just have to enforce the law.

Father forgive them ... I'll give that lad credit where it's due – he was a bit different at least. Maybe that's why I remember him. There we were, gambling for his things, dicing for our *little extras* as we call them, and he says, *Father, forgive them, for they don't know what they're doing.*

Most of them are too shocked or in too much pain to say anything. They just stay there, pinned and moaning, trying to lift themselves up so they can keep breathing. Some of them pour curses down on us. Now I get *that*. That's what I'd do. And some of them pray to their helpless little god.

But this one was different. *Father, forgive them*... Imagine that.

It's funny. Ever since he said it, all I can think of is my own dad. A bit of a sod to be honest and we never really got on. He was forever going on about foreigners, about how their dirty ways were going to take over. How they'd bring the world crashing down. When I was little he just seemed so angry.

But he always tried to put family first. And I remember how, when I was little, he came rushing out of the house once when a bunch of older lads were beating me up. He seemed huge to me then. And probably to those lads too. They ran off. And he scooped me up in his arms and asked me if I was all right. It was the kindest thing he ever did. And I loved him for it.

But – and this is the mad thing – I also hated him for it. I hated him because instead of hugging me and seeing if I was all right, I wanted him to run off and beat up those boys. I wanted him to take revenge for me ... because I couldn't. Because I was too little. Because it would take years before I'd be big enough to take the bullies on …

And this fool on a cross says *Father forgive them…* I don't know who he was talking to. Does it matter? Maybe he was just delirious. But here's a bloke who'd been beaten, tortured and nailed up and he asks his father to forgive us. If it was me I'd be asking my dad to take revenge. I'd be asking him to take on a world I was too weak to change.

What he said frightens me. I mean, imagine a world that forgives torturers and haters and the violent. There's part of me that despises – no, hates – him for asking for forgiveness for us … for those who hurt him.

And there's a part of me that will love him – this stranger whose name I never knew – till my dying day.

TRULY I TELL YOU, TODAY YOU WILL BE WITH ME IN PARADISE

If I had the breath left I'd laugh. If it wasn't agony I'd smile. And if I had my life again I might even change …

I've lived my life as if I had forever. Maybe because I never cared for tomorrow, I never got past today. And now all I have is today …

I'm not good. I've cheated and lied and stolen. I did a terrible thing to end up here. I murdered a woman. But that wasn't the worst. I did other things to her as well. I got caught and I got what I deserved.

And I accept that. That's the strange advantage of being someone like me: you know what's coming to you if you get caught, just as you know what you'll get if it goes well. I've lived like a king and I've been a beggar … I was born on a rubbish pit and I'll die on one …

And I could be like the bastard over there – shouting and cursing and having a go at the only innocent sod on this mound. Except I'm out of time. What's the use of pretending I'm anything other than I am any more?

I've never believed you can tell whether someone is good or bad from the look of their face. I've seen it all, you see. I've met baby-faced killers and beautiful women who'd cut your throat as soon as look at you. I've known ugly hulking giants of men who are as innocent as lambs.

But this man, the one they nailed up between us, is different. I'd heard of him and only heard good things. But if you went on appearances you'd say he was as nasty as me. They've done a proper job on him – smashed his face and body bad, one of his eyes is closed. He looks like an ugly piece of work.

I just knew when he looked at me with his good eye that he shouldn't have been dying with us, that he'd done nothing wrong. And that piece of crap that other side of us was taunting and mocking him, and despite the pain, I'd had enough …

So I shouted, with all I had left, and I told him to shut it … and for the first time in forever there was no bull in what I said. I had nothing to lose or gain. There were no lies and tricks. And despite the fact I was dying it felt good.

Just once in my life I'd done the right thing. I don't even know why I said it ... *Jesus, remember me when you come into your kingdom ...*

And then he was speaking and saying an impossible thing ... *Amen, I tell you, today you will be with me in paradise ...*

And I was crying ... not in pain, or fear or anything ... For I know everything about bullshit and trickery and lies ... and I've used them to do nasty things ... and all I deserve is contempt and punishment ... And there was no deceit in this man ...

His voice was as true and kind as my mother's when I'd been little. Before everything went wrong ...

No one could save me from my fate. But he had. I was dead but I was never more alive ...

And now they're coming to break my legs ... and I'm scared because I know there's another justice to face ... but I'm with him and he's with me. And it's time. And for the first time I've found someone I can trust.

WOMAN, HERE IS YOUR SON

Life has taught me one thing: laughter is as close to tears as a mother is to her son.

When he said those words, *Woman, here is your son*, I almost laughed. Despite all my tears, I actually almost laughed. Because, of all the things he could have said, these words seemed the most unwanted, the most absurd.

You know what I wanted to hear, don't you? I wanted to hear him proclaim his love for me, his mother. *Mum, I love you for all time. Mum I'm so sorry it came to this.* Yes, I even wanted to hear, *Mum I've let you down. I'm sorry.* Because there's part of me, the part of me that wanted him to be a normal boy, an ordinary man with a wife and kids, that wanted him to say sorry for all he's put me through.

And he says, *Woman, here is your son,* nodding over at that skinny kid John, the eager one with the spots. And then he looks at John and says, *Look, here is your mother.*

I died then. I'm almost ashamed to admit that, face to face as I was with my son's real death. But I did die then. Or something died within me. Something I'd been holding on to for all those years: the stupid hope that somehow he'd find a way to turn back from the path he'd been on.

But when he said those words, I knew I'd lost him. Completely. My first-born son. My treasure. The child who'd quickened me to joy and pain.

Until that point, a tiny part of me – the secret me, the bit that was still the young and hopeful girl who'd borne this man thirty years before – still thought that even if he died young, he would die as the person I'd dreamt he'd be: just an ordinary man who loved and cursed and made babies and worked and moaned about how hard life was, like everyone else.

This man was not dying as my son. It was like he was … becoming something else. I'm still not sure what. Maybe he was becoming all of us. And so somehow all of us were dying that day.

When he spoke to me, *Mother, here is your son,* I died too. And my boy – my brilliant, erratic boy who'd fallen out of trees as a child, who'd scraped his knees and cried and come to me for comfort – was gone.

And I was gone too. We were all gone.

MY GOD, WHY HAVE YOU FORSAKEN ME? (1)

A knife in my heart. That's what they were. For they were my words too.

In my head – and, I know, only in my head – he was speaking for me. Because they've so often been my words. Like him I might still be saying them on my last day.

But unlike Jesus my story is hardly known. Even my name changes depending on who you talk to. I am Shulamith, but most people know me as Salome.

From the moment I was born I was unwanted. I was a girl. And my parents couldn't afford another girl. So they took me out to the wilderness and left me to die.

How could they? It's a question I've learnt not to ask. They did and that's the end of it.

From the moment I was born I was abandoned. I was forsaken. And the couple who found me and took me in, as generous as I tell myself they were, sometimes made me wish they'd left me in the wilderness to die.

The couple who raised me – my mum and dad for all practical purposes – did their best, but it was clear from early on that I was there to help out more than to be loved. They reminded me again and again that I wasn't theirs.

From the moment I could understand their words it was clear they were unsure whether they'd made the right decision. They were shepherds. They lived a hard life away from towns and cities. And they had a son already who they dreamed I'd marry. The apple of their eye.

And as I grew I found that loneliness has layers – that living out in the lonely places was more often bleak than inspiring, whatever the prophets say about finding God out there. And being a shepherd is hardly a recipe for popularity. And I had my dreams – of finding my way to a place where I was wanted and cared for.

I ran away when I could. I was not made to be a wife and it was all I could do to fight off my brother's advances. He wasn't bad or mad. He was as lonely as me and his mum and dad had set him up. I ran away into the night, abandoning my family and glad of the dark. For I knew its contours now. If it tried to swallow me whole I could fight back.

Eventually I found my way to him – to Jesus and his little band of fools and dreamers. I will not say what I had to do to survive along the way, but it taught me new faces of loneliness. In his company, for the first time, I began to feel I was home.

I wasn't a fool. I was careful. Like a wild animal that comes for scraps I let down my guard slowly, each day drawing closer, till I allowed someone to reach out and befriend me. But even when I felt part of his family, there was always that bit of me on the lookout for danger … for rejection. I'd been abandoned too long.

And of course there's always that bit of you that you secretly treasure – that you keep for yourself. That bit which says, *They'll never understand*. Not one of them. No matter how hard their life has been. And as much as I loved Jesus, I thought the same about him. What did he know about being abandoned?

I am Shulamith. I am Salome. I am all the girls and women who have ever been abandoned and cut off from safety. And when I saw him crucified, and when he said those words, Jesus was me and I was him. And, for that day, he was all of us.

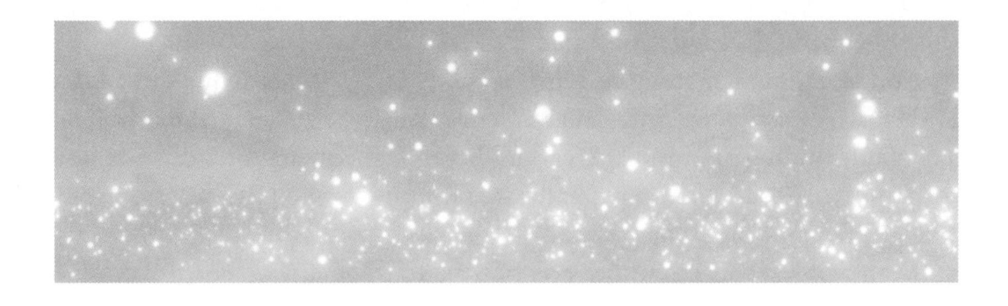

MY GOD, WHY HAVE YOU FORSAKEN ME? (2)

He'd always talked about God as his father. He asked us to do the same.

Indeed, he went further than that. He talked about God as *abba* – as dad or dada. Like he was just a toddler being led by the hand.

That might have been all right for him, but it was too much for the rest of us. Father … maybe … just maybe … but *abba*? No. As if God – the almighty – could ever be that close to us. As if we could ever be that close to him.

Maybe that's why those words – *My God, my God, why have you forsaken me?* – hit us so hard. Pretty much everyone had abandoned him already. His so-called mates had fled into the night. And there was just us, really – a few women who would not let this thing happen to him alone.

Maybe it was just safer for us to be there than the men. We were just women after all. Or maybe we understood something the men could not – about loneliness, about how close birth is to death, about the shape of life and living and dying. That's why they've always been scared of us – because we remind them of the thing they want to deny: that they cannot escape death.

But he'd always seemed different. He'd always seemed so sure. His bond with his God, his father, his dad, had always been the heart of him. And in his agony he screamed, *My God, why have you forsaken me?* The clever men, the temple men who came to make sure he was doomed, laughed then, said he was wasting his time quoting the psalms. The Lord wouldn't save him.

But we heard something else. It was the sound of the God he'd lived with all his life dying for him. Dying inside him. It was the sound of a human being alone and abandoned. It was the cry of a child left in the wilderness to die. Of an innocent baby slaughtered in the night.

When they tortured him they tried to take everything from him. That was the point of the torture. And it was as if in this moment they'd won.

I'm not so sure. He always said that the seed had to fall and die to release new life.

He was not afraid of us women. He was almost one of us. In that moment I felt he was as close to us as he'd ever been.

One kind of God died for him on the cross. One kind of God abandoned him. But we did not. We stood by him. As the old God died, a new one was born. Born between us and him. In the relationship. A God who stands by us in our hour of need, and we by him … by her.

I AM THIRSTY

Human beings are so predictable. You tickle them and they laugh. You smile at them and most times they smile back. You beat them and they cry out. Beat them long enough, and they'll do anything to make it stop.

I am thirsty. How many times have I heard them say that? Almost all of them say it in the end. Human beings are so predictable.

When I became a soldier all I wanted to do was travel, fight, get laid. And they send me here. To the backside of the Empire. And all we do is try to keep down troublemakers like this. And all I do is nail them up and listen to their damn moaning and their *I am thirsties*.

I'm sick of it. Sick to my soul of it.

I am thirsty. I could break his legs now. Just to be done with it.

Don't all these people know that I'm thirsty too? That I want things too?

Doing this … I won't call it a job … doing this to other human beings disgusts me. Makes me disgusted with my leaders. With this world. With myself. This is not what I became a soldier for.

Violence I was ready for – for the sake of protecting the Empire. But torture? And the rumour is that this man has done nothing wrong except say that humans should be free to be their true selves. Is it so wrong to believe that?

Tell me there is something more to life than this. Something more than men beating up other men and women and nailing them to bits of wood and turning them into human trees creaking in the wind until there is nothing left in them but *I am thirsty.*

Tell me, please. Tell me that there is something, just a hint of something good. Something pure. Like a baby's smile. Like a man with clean hands. Like this man dying on a tree. Like a love in this world which can bring us home.

IT IS FINISHED

Why throw your life away on a stupid dream? That's what he said to me – my father Zebedee – that day James and I walked out of Capernaum trailing after Jesus.

Why throw your life away …

Me and my friends – Peter, Andrew, my brother James, Mary of Magdala, all the rest – have seen things you could never dream of. We've seen the dead raised to life. We've seen poor people given riches beyond their dreams. We've seen children given hope, and learned that if we're truly to know God we must become like children.

Don't tell me I've thrown my life away.

There's so much that Jesus said and did that I don't understand. He called us his numbskulls sometimes, with a grin on his face.

But this is something else – his death. He'd hinted at it, talked about it for months. We just laughed or ignored what he said. None of us ever really believed it was going to happen. How could someone as wonderful as him die? And die a criminal's death.

But it has happened. The man who gave us everything – my lord and king, my friend, the person I'd die for – is dead.

And those final words. *It is finished.*

It is finished. I don't understand. They frighten me. They're ice in my heart. I just can't figure them out.

Does he mean that's it? Does he mean we should give up everything we've dreamed of? That we've reached the end of the road and should just go home and start fishing the lake again? Ha, my dad would love that. I can hear him now – *I told you so. Wasting your life on fools' dreams* – as he throws me a net to mend.

How can I, how can any of us, go back? We are not – none of us will ever be – the same. We can't just pretend that the world can go back to the way it used to be. The threads of our old lives have been scattered.

It is finished. Did he mean something else? That something is completed? *It is finished* could mean *It is completed*, couldn't it?

But what? And how can this death complete anything that's good or holy or hopeful?

Jesus used to talk sometimes about the good shepherd. About how the good shepherd would lay his life down for his sheep. We used to laugh at this. All the shepherds I've ever known are useless good-for-nothings who wouldn't lay their lives down for anyone but themselves.

But Jesus would smile back and say that the good shepherd would be the one to lay down his life for his sheep. And then he'd grin and say more than that: that he'd lay down his life for his friends.

Is this what he's done here today?

FATHER, INTO YOUR HANDS I COMMEND MY SPIRIT

You think you're better than me? You think you wouldn't get carried away? You think you wouldn't fall into line?

Well, you weren't there, in that crowd with all the shouting and jeering and baying for blood.

I didn't know this man. I'd never met him, not to speak to anyway. I'd heard of him, of course, the rumours and the stories. I'd heard him speak once. The usual nonsense these boys talk about, how God is coming to save us and set us free. Pur-leese!

And I'd been there when he'd gone mad in the Temple. I saw how crazy he was then. What he was prepared to do. He wasn't all talk, I have to give him that.

He turned my stall over. Without a moment's consideration to my livelihood or needs. Like a stupid little thug. Like all these thugs treat a woman trying to make an honest living.

So, yes, I was angry. Maybe I was pleased when they took him in. Maybe I jeered extra hard. But the idiot deserved it. People like him need to be taught a lesson. They need to be taught some respect. So don't judge me for giving him a hard time. Life is hard enough without mindless young men going on the rampage.

And when the crowd started baying for his blood, you bet I did the same. Have you ever been in a crowd? Have you ever felt your blood rise? And, yes, it felt good. I'm not going to lie to you. All my pent-up frustration I poured out on him. When they nailed him up I jeered with the loudest of them. And maybe I'd do so again. It felt good. To get it all out.

Except for one thing.

Just before he died he said, *Father, into your hands I commend my spirit.* I don't know why it's stuck with me. It wasn't like he said it dramatically – like you might think a king would, giving his final words for all time. The way he spoke, it was almost the exact opposite.

He spoke like a kid would, using a child's words. *Dada, into your hands I give my spirit.*

I've heard people talk about how the world can stand still. About how it gets stuck or they get stuck and then it's like they can't move on. You know, when a person loses someone they love and that's it – for them it's the end of the world. I've never really believed that, but maybe at that moment I got a glimpse.

Those words – a little boy's words – are the saddest words I've ever heard. It was like hearing your own child's death, and their need for comfort and love and trust. And you want to help them, but you can't.

He broke my heart then. My heart will never be the same again.

OTHER STORIES AND POEMS

Stories of passion and resurrection (whether invested with transcendent meaning or not) are very difficult to avoid. Some will argue that narratives that involve heroes/heroines travelling through trial and death towards new life are hardwired into reality and culture. Some Christians might argue that this is because passion and resurrection are fundamental to the world's structure and Jesus directs and focuses our attention on this truth. Whatever the case, it's true that both popular and high culture, cinema, novels and visual art constantly play with tropes of death and new life.

The following stories attempt to work broadly with notions of passion and resurrection. I've sought to centre them on voices which are, perhaps, rarely heard in church contexts, even in these increasingly liberal times. The use of humour might strike an awkward tone for some, but it is grounded in an attempt to reckon with the black humour that sometimes emerges in bleak and challenging situations. The intention of both the more humorous and the visceral stories is to play with abiding themes of death and new life in ways which – in church contexts at least – break unusual ground. Some readers may find some of the language crude and offensive. It is not my intention to offend or outrage, but – as I have indicated in places like my book *Dazzling Darkness* – to indicate that there are places and experiences where blasphemy is prayer and prayer is blasphemy.

Equally, the small selection of poetry attempts to respond to passion and resurrection with an appreciation for the differing forms they can take. Given my own experience of chronic illness it is perhaps unsurprising that I am fascinated by medical pictures of what new life might look like. If the poems are not drawn exclusively from the varieties of passion and resurrection experienced by the chronically and acutely ill, they are grounded in them.

THE DIRT PIT

'What yer doing?'

'Nothing,' said God.

'You are! Are you making mud pies?' replied the girl.

'Might be,' said God, between working away at the soil with his trowel.

'Aw, can I help?'

'If you like,' said God with a shrug, 'but I'm just digging really.'

'But we can make mud pies later, can't we?' the girl asked excitedly.

'Yeah, why not!'

And so the girl ran off home to get her favourite bucket and spade and together the two children dug deeper into the rich, soft ground. After they'd been working for a while a young boy turned up.

'What yer doing?' said the boy.

'Nothing,' said God and the girl together.

'You are! What yer digging that hole for?'

'Just 'cos,' replied the girl.

'Oh,' said the boy. 'Can I help?'

'Yeah, all right,' replied God.

'Yes!' exclaimed the boy, and with that he rushed off to beg, borrow or steal something to dig with.

It was hard work, but they loved it. With the three of them working together the little hole was becoming quite a ditch. And slowly, but surely, they were getting absolutely covered in dirt. Every now and then another kid would wander by, curious, and would end up pitching in. Swelling the size of the pit, piling the soil up on the sides until you couldn't see them any more. Just digging because it was there to be done. Laughing and giggling and screaming, throwing earthworms at each other. On through the afternoon they dug, laughing so much their fizzy pop came streaming out through their noses. Until, exhausted, they fell back against the walls of their massive, glorious hole and looked in awe at each other for what they'd done. After a little while, God said, with a twinkle in his eyes, 'Let's make some mud pies.'

Of course, what the children had done hadn't gone unnoticed. After all, this pit was dug in local parkland overseen by a hundred different houses. This was not the place to dig a hole if you wanted to keep it private. So there were the usual twitched curtains and, in front gardens, neighbours exchanged comments. Some, who thought what the children was doing was amusing, said, 'Let them play,' while others got increasingly annoyed. How dare these children tear up our little park! All were puzzled: what could be the point of digging this ditch? The mumbling and grumbling rumbled on through much of the afternoon until someone, nobody was quite sure who, had had enough. For when two bobbies turned up, it was obvious that someone had called the police.

The two PCs ambled slowly over to the big pile of earth, from which hidden giggles and shouts were coming, and peered in. They saw a dozen kids or more, covered in dirt and mud, laughing and throwing bits of mud pie at each other. Then, first one, then another and then another of the children realised that two police officers were towering over them. And how they towered. The giggling died down and mud fell quietly from chubby fingers on to the pit's floor. For a moment there was stillness until the terror of being hauled in front of mum by the police shot through a dozen childish minds. The mad scramble to escape began. They pulled and pushed their way past each other any way they could, each doing their level best to avoid being caught by a police officer's searching hands. As the girl who'd been the first to join God did her best to make her escape, the policewoman made a grab to stop her. But at the moment the officer was about to make contact, the girl dived away. And, as she ran, she screamed back, 'It's his fault. It's all his fault.'

God stood quietly and calmly in the hole he and the others had dug for themselves. As he looked into the eyes of the uniformed adults he knew he was in trouble, but was ready to face it. After all, he was only a kid and the trouble he was in wasn't that bad. He'd live through it easily enough. But he began to cry nonetheless. Not, as the officers assumed, through fear of what his parents were going to say, but because God saw clearly for the first time what the future might hold. Because he saw that he was in love with a world that could not accept him. Because he saw that though he might bring people together in delight and communion, in ways that were simple, powerful and profound, there would always be some who would see him and his friends as a threat. And most of all, he saw that when childish troubles became adult ones and, inevitably, he dug much bigger, more dangerous holes for himself, his friends, like young children, would desert him and leave him to be pushed out of the world, alone.

THE IMAGE OF GOD

Everyone knows the story of how, come the Seventh Day, God had pretty much created everything. Humans, squid, rocks, fat, thin, big and small things. It's less well known that she'd also invented the movies. Or film cameras, at least. You see, God loves the movies. And while you might expect her to like *The Sound of Music* and stuff of that ilk – and, indeed, she is a fan in a camp, postmodern sort of way – singing nuns always slightly unnerve her. She's not taken with biblical epics either; she's never said why, but some of the angels reckon it's because she wasn't offered a big enough part. No, God loves gangster films. You might be the creator of the universe, but there's no accounting for taste.

So God created film and, on the Seventh Day, set about making the first home video, spending most of her time taking very dull, out-of-focus shots of pot plants and the living room and getting puzzled angels and any passing creature to have stilted conversations about where they were going on their holidays. The centipedes, who had no concept of holidays, were particularly dull. But God enjoyed herself and couldn't wait for someone to have a wedding. Perhaps she'd go and see the humans …

God wasn't quite sure whether to show her new invention to her beloved. She knew they'd love it, would share her fun and joy, maybe even make an award-winning film with her, but there was something that made her want to hold back. Some nagging doubt about the implications of human free will. But since she could no more pinpoint that doubt than figure out why Arnold Schwarzenegger had managed to have such a long career, she pushed it into the background and entered the Garden. She just stood there for a while watching them, simply enjoying their grace and lack of self-consciousness, barely able to withhold her delight. Yes, she would share her new creation with them and they would make great movies together.

So it was that Adam and Eve, in their innocence, learnt about the moving image. It was only later that they learnt about its power. For now, all was joy and light in the Garden, and God and her friends made freewheeling, experimental films together and tried to master the art of a good fade to black.

But one day, as God was ambling through the Garden, practising her best Travis Bickle impression, she noticed something was wrong. Or, rather, she realised something was dreadfully wrong. Something had been wrong for a while. Adam, in particular, had become less and less enthusiastic about their regular film shoots. The times when the three of them sat out under the stars, munching popcorn and watching their latest work had become rare. The joy and fun had gone out of it all and Eve and Adam appeared more interested in themselves than anything else. At first, God had thought this was because they'd taken up her suggestion to try for a family – if so, it was only natural that they'd want to spend time alone together. However, when Adam suggested that God shouldn't come round so often, that maybe she'd better things to do, she'd been shaken.

God was cut to the quick, but she obeyed their wishes. She loved them too much to force herself upon them and only the hope that one day they would welcome her back could assuage her loneliness. Her visits became infrequent and when she came they never made films together, although it was obvious that Eve and Adam had acquired a mass of equipment and had tapes and film spools everywhere. They'd come up with something called 'television', which God thought sounded like a laugh, but they wouldn't share it with her. Yes, things had been bad for a long time. But today was something else.

The Garden was silent. Or, rather, its usual sounds were absent. There was a faint, unfamiliar background noise, a low hum that increased as she approached Adam and Eve's home. On impulse, God decided to creep up quietly and surprise them. As she closed in, she had the shock of her life – a voice boomed from all around her, 'INTRUDER, INTRUDER,' on and on, punctuated by high-pitched buzzing sounds. Before she could compose herself, God was confronted by Adam and Eve, faces full of threat. Behind them she could now see the cause of the low hum – piles of equipment, video cameras and wires everywhere.

'It's called CCTV,' said Eve. 'We saw you miles away. Don't think you can hide from us.'

'But why?' replied God. 'What's this about? Eve … Adam … tell me ..'

Adam looked firmly into God's eyes and said, 'It's about us. It's about why you're not welcome here any more. Most of all it's about the Image. About its power. You kept it back from us, but we found out. And now we're in control.'

God was confused. 'What are you on about? Hold on, is this a wind-up? You sound like a villain from a James Bond film.'

'No. It's no wind-up,' responded Eve. 'You hid us from ourselves. You kept us innocent and unaware. But we found out, about who we are. Film showed us we have an image and that image can be controlled. Must be controlled, because if you don't do it, somebody else will. Whoever controls the image has power, and power is control.'

'Come on,' cried God. 'Listen to yourselves. Who's writing your script? George Lucas? This is madness. (Listen to me – now I'm at it.)'

'It's reality,' said Adam calmly, 'Come, we'll show you.'

And God was led into an area they called the Control Room.

'Let me demonstrate,' said Adam. 'Here we have you wandering through the Garden. An innocent scene, yes? But, if I shift to this view, here, it looks very different doesn't it? It wouldn't be hard to make the case that you were breaking in on us. Don't you see? How things are depend on how they look. Whoever controls the image controls reality. Controls you, even.'

Adam flicked a switch and a large club appeared in the hand of the picture of God showing on the screen.

'It's fake, yes, but it looks real. And it's how it looks that matters … Don't you see the potential? The power. And you would have kept it all from us.'

'No,' stuttered God, 'it wasn't meant to be like that ...'

But Eve interrupted, 'But the image is dangerous. And that's why we've had to take precautions. The CCTV. The "technology". Since anyone can manipulate your image, you have to stay ahead of the game, make sure you're in control. We shall always be as we want to be. Better still, others will be as we want them to be.'

'You're mad,' said God.

'And you, my old mate, are surplus baggage,' added Adam. 'Now here's what we're going to do for you,' he continued. 'Leave now and never come back. Do it and we'll leave you alone. Come back, try to interfere and, well, let's just say we can make you in any image we want, can't we? Come to think of it, we probably shall.'

Then, in a mock act of sweetness, Adam and Eve put their arms round each other and, together, waved to God, saying (in their sweetest voices), 'Goodbye!'

God was devastated. She could barely take it in. Why this rejection? Why so much fear? And they were wrong about one thing: it had never been her plan to keep them as children, as innocents. Her deepest desire had been for them to be their own people. If she'd had a plan at all it had been to encourage them to achieve that without losing their playfulness, their sense of the mischievous and absurd. To always remember what it was to be a child, even within a world of responsibilities. Not this – this grown-up-ness consumed with seriousness, self and fear. Cynicism masquerading as maturity.

'In "discovering themselves",' God thought sadly, 'they've lost themselves. All they've got is images and masks. And that's why they fear me – I can see who they are, beyond the surfaces. If only they'd let me.' God's pain was a funeral in heaven and earth, and creation mourned. She felt consumed by anguish. Not so much for herself, but for her beloved children, these exiles to themselves. Who thought they'd gained control and taken possession of the keys of heaven, but rather had thrown themselves into the wilderness without comfort or guide. Without realising it. How she wanted to help them, now that they were more like children than ever, more ignorant of themselves than they could believe. Her heart went out to them. So God left Eden for the last time and headed for no place special. She'd never wanted to go there.

It was the wilderness. For God, for them all. A rootless wandering as God sought her people, tried to gather them to herself. But they couldn't or wouldn't listen, no matter whom she sent. For the children of Eve and Adam were many and distractions plentiful and the voice of God faint against the shouts of the great gods the people made for themselves. As for Adam and Eve, things hadn't worked out quite as they'd planned. The power hadn't come. For they couldn't keep control – too many people wanted a piece of the action and the world ripped itself apart in wars over how people imagined they should appear to each other or imagined others to be. So, Adam and Eve had grown soft and fat on too many potato chips and cheap beer, experts of the remote control and little else. Consumed by the world of the image, of channel-surfing, fifteen minutes of fame and video game wars. Images in need of constant renewal.

Adam shouted to Eve, 'Get me a beer, will ya?'

'Get it yourself, slob,' came a voice from the kitchen.

As usual, Adam was watching TV. 'This Jeremy Kyle bloke is a prat,' he thought. 'Not as bad as his guests tho'. "I trap men by getting pregnant." Scum.'

He started to surf, but all he found was the usual junk. He paused for a minute on a game show as the presenter asked, 'In the Bible, what is the name of the first woman?'

'Damn, I know this, I know this,' thought Adam, but frustration got the better of him and he gave up. So he flicked on, through scenes of war and hunger, talking heads and daytime soaps. And, then, something made him stop. A face. Someone he'd seen before, in another time. A face rising like ghost from another, almost forgotten life. He stopped and watched; watched a handheld, live news shot of a man dying on a cross. The Image of God.

OUR HOUSE

Houses have lives of their own. It's just that the life of a building is so slow you hardly notice it. But it's there nonetheless. The Spirit of God is with even a house and where the Spirit is, life follows: the life that winds its way through the rocks and minerals and creatures that were called forth at the earth's birth. Carrying an ancient, holy memory ready to sing again God's wondrous song.

Our house, the one we're interested in, was deeply unhappy. If she were human you would say she'd fallen on hard times, or even that the hard times had fallen on her. She looked dreadful. And since the estate had started falling apart, this was not a good place to be a house – especially an old one like her. In just three or four years the area had gone from somewhere you really wanted to live to a dump: half of the properties were empty and boarded up, or burnt out, and gangs of kids were stirring trouble. The estate had never been perfect, but it had never been like this. Everyone had an explanation for the decline. Except our house. She didn't know or care. It was stuff beyond her. She just felt the pain.

She'd been a fine house once; nothing pretentious or stuck-up, just an honest-to-goodness terrace, two-up two-down, with the loo outdoors. She remembered the soot that had fallen from the sky and blackened the whole street and the human who'd tickled her front step with the daily scrubbing. She'd felt fresh and loved, new and young then. And, with the passing years, the humans who lived in her put new wallpaper up and did a bathroom conversion. Double-glazing, even. All right, these things won't change the world, but they mattered to her. That seemed a long time ago though. For one day the humans were gone and the other things they'd put inside her disappeared too. Others came, it's true, but they didn't stay long and never put new wallpaper up (some of them even ripped it off). As the damp rose cold through her walls and no one repaired her roof, she began to feel very old, ill and tired.

The day came when no humans lived in her any more. All that was left were lots of bits and bobs. She was quite alone. One night, some humans smashed her door in and, laughing, made a light that burned deep into her walls and floors. Eating everything inside her and making soot thicker than any she'd known. The water the other humans sprayed on her offered no soothing. The flames were ended, but the silence and numbness that followed were terrifying. This house was a house no longer.

All that remained within her, the bricks and mortar, concrete and wood, longed for the end. But the agony stretched on, as she was boarded up and signs placed all over her. As time passed the humans got used to her scarred remains and she almost forgot who she was. Then, one day, she sensed humans taking an interest again, humans in yellow hats and jackets, with prodding hands and a big thing with a ball and chain. She felt a hand push against her and knew that another part of her walls had fallen away, joining the long-accumulating mess. Perhaps this was it, then. The end. She no longer cared – the hope and promise which had seen her made and in which she'd shared was long gone, packed away, perhaps, in the suitcases of the vanished people who had once made her home. The end when it came was dusty, noisy and brief, and none of those who watched had come to mourn or give thanks, but to stare.

And there the story ends. Well, almost. The demolition was part of a bigger plan – to renew the area, to somehow take the dry, dead bones of the estate and breathe new life into it again. Unexpectedly our house became central to this story too. For on that first demolition day, as the dust began to settle, someone had the thought to take a few bricks from the rubble and keep them for future use. And when the time came for buildings to go up, these few bricks found their place as cornerstones in some of the new houses. Of course, for us, these things are important as symbols, as reminders that we shouldn't forget the past. But for those few bricks it was so much more. For deep within them, the Spirit was stirring. Stirring an ancient song that welled up through the minerals, rocks and creatures from which these tired, cheap bricks had been made, into and beyond the story of our house. Kindling the ember of hope that always remains in the Spirit's presence, allowing our house to begin again God's wondrous song.

THE BLEEDING[2]

She couldn't remember which she'd heard first – the rumours of a young Rabbi healing the sick and bringing good news to the poor or the story of the bleeding woman who'd suddenly been healed by him. It didn't really matter. She'd taken note. Perhaps it was what people said about Jesus – about how he wasn't afraid of being close to the unclean, the untouchables. Perhaps it was just the fact that someone else, with a curse like her own, had been healed. After all, people like her didn't get healed. Yet everyone said that it had happened. So she'd begun to hope. And she knew she had to seek this man out, hardly a difficult task even for an outcast like her. All she had to do was listen to the words on everyone's lips and follow the word of mouth until it drew close to him. For whether they loved or hated him, everyone was talking about Jesus.

At first, she couldn't make him out. A large crowd was following and surrounding him. Overwhelming him, she thought. If he's there. She realised she had no idea what he looked like. What was she doing here anyway? This was no place for her – with people, with clean people, whole people. What was she thinking of, coming here? Of course, he'd take no notice of her – what man ever had? She was outcast, unfit to be with men, unfit to be a wife or mother. No one came near her – not even women, for fear of getting her curse. No, this was no place for her. She should go. But as she was leaving, she caught sight of him – just the back of his head, but she knew it was him. And she had faith and knew she could go on. And she started to push her way through the crowds, shutting out the indignant words spat her way, pressing on towards her goal before her faith ran out. Until he was there, so close she could touch him.

---

[2] First published in Rachel Mann, *Dazzling Darkness* (Glasgow: Wild Goose 2012).

'Get back, woman' – a voice, then a man's face aimed at her. 'Don't bother the Rabbi today.' As he said this, the man she just knew was Jesus stopped walking and turned to face her. Incredibly, like an army under orders, everyone else stopped too. Stopped and seemed to turn their attention towards her. Jesus said, 'Andrew, leave her be.' Silence. Or so it seemed. All she could think was, 'He looks so tired.' Tired and troubled. Like her father had once looked when she was a child – the look of one waiting for the debt-collectors to come and take everything. She didn't know what to do. She wanted to speak, to ask for mercy, but all she could do was stand before him quietly crying. He opened his mouth, as if to speak, moved forward, as if to hold her, but something stopped him. And instead of words of peace or an embrace of welcome, he looked into her eyes with a gaze she could not fathom. Mouth half open. Tired, painful eyes. A look that seemed to mark the beginning and end of all he had to say to her, for as he gave it he began to draw back and turn to go. Leaving her standing there. Leaving everyone puzzled and silent. And as he moved, they moved, leaving her alone on the road. Humiliated. Confused. Unclean. With nowhere left to go.

Nowhere left to go. 'Bastard,' she thought. 'How could he do it to me? What kind of a person does that? In front of all those people. Surely not a Messiah. Not a king. Just another man with a following. A magician who'd run out of tricks. He'd nothing to say. In front of all those people he'd nothing to say. He couldn't even touch me. Why couldn't he touch me? Why couldn't he care for me? Why couldn't he heal me? If even half the things they said about him were true, he could have healed me.' She just wanted to be well and she'd had faith. He could have made her well, but he didn't. 'Bastard', she thought. Humiliated in front of all those people. Where could she go from here? Run after him down the road? Confront him? But what was the point? She'd never get anywhere near him, not this time, and, anyway, she'd be a laughing-stock. The one he wouldn't heal. Too much shame. And how could she go back home? It'd be even worse. Yet where else was there to go? It offered shelter, at least. She was tired. She'd dared to hope, she'd acted in hope. Her hope had died. She went home.

Home. A hovel away from the clean and good. Yet it wasn't much of a place for hiding. For as the truth got out, that she'd been to Jesus but not been healed, the mockery became more nasty than any she'd ever known. Mothers singled her out, frightening their children with tales that they'd end up like her if they were bad or faithless. Not just outcast, but cut off from the mercy of God. Even those who were like her, the unclean who lived around her, kept their distance and shouted insults. This faithless woman. Until she hid herself from others more completely than ever before, filling her time rearing the hate and anger that had been born to her on the road. Tenderly nurturing the spite fathered by Jesus. Aimed at Jesus. Waiting for Jesus.

And wait she would, sensing hate, like a tumour, growing within her; but the waiting time was shorter than she'd imagined. The opportunity for revenge arrived, like a fever, unexpectedly and barely announced. For the 'King of the Jews' had pushed his luck just too far. In front of all the wrong people in the city down the road. Because he just couldn't resist riding in triumph into Jerusalem, provoking the Romans and the religious with his grand claims, and disrupting the life of the Temple. But, like all false Messiahs, his cause had burnt itself out, the crowds had turned against him and he'd been arrested. And 'Joy,' she thought, 'he's going to be crucified on a rubbish dump outside the city wall.' This she had to see. Had to be part of. If only there was time. So she asked God to grant her this moment of blessing, that she might play her part, that she might watch him die.

Oh, happy day! Happy day. It was so long since she'd felt like this. Like a prisoner set free, like the blind man given sight, like the child she'd once been. No stumbling for her today; today was her day. Her life would be her own today. For one day. Yet, in the end, after her urgent journey, the rubbish dump crucifixion wasn't quite how she'd expected it to be. For she couldn't muster the dignified entrance she'd planned, so hot and sweaty had she become. Nor was there much of a crowd: just a few women and soldiers and passers-by. And the two others nailed to crosses. A poor audience for a denunciation. And she hadn't expected the place to feel like this. Like decay. Like winter earth getting ready for a new crop. Most of all, she hadn't expected to feel this scared, to feel that she could lose her nerve at any moment. She thought she would laugh she was so out of her depth. Quietly, she approached his cross.

It was a commonplace brutality. A hundred petty fanatics had ended this way. But, in meeting him like this, she could barely cope. He was a naked, failing, blood-and-shit-oozing piece of sweat. Marked out by nails, already dead, even if each shattered breath insisted otherwise. His was a bruised face and closed eyes created by skilled, unseen hands. Surely he was beyond sense. And she felt like she was carrying a message she could barely own – long since memorised, worn down, no longer her own. 'Perhaps if I start,' she thought. 'If I get it over and done with.' But what was the point? He was little more than a corpse. No point in screaming at a corpse. Bastard. He'd got away, again. Anger flowed up within her like a spring of living water.

'Bastard … you complete fucking bastard,' she screamed, 'you piece of shit, you lying piece of shit, just die, just get on and die …' On and on, she screamed.

Slowly, Jesus raised his head and opened his mouth as if to speak. Painfully, he mumbled something like, 'Father, forgive them for they know not what they do.'

'What's that?' she said, 'Forgive them? Forgive me? You arrogant shit. It's you who should be begging forgiveness. After lording it over others, for playing at being Messiah.' Her voice dropped. 'For what you've done to me … what you didn't do for me.' She fell silent, then almost to herself, 'Why couldn't you heal me? Why me?' She began to cry. Undignified. Uncontrolled. An ancient, animal pain breaking the surface.

Eventually, she looked at the cross again, expecting, hoping he'd be dead.

That would be some sort of end, at least. But he wasn't. He was looking at her. She was sure of that. Not the look he'd given on the road; he couldn't muster that. This was more of a glance through a half-opened eye, but he was looking at her nonetheless. 'Got your attention at last, have I?' she thought. 'Well, fuck you. I don't need you. You're not a saviour; you're just some piece of shit on a cross.' Still he looked at her. Through dying eyes. No longer waiting for the debt-collectors to come and take everything. They'd been and gone and this mess on the cross was what they'd left. Still he stared. On and on as if he daren't let go. This effort directed at her. Reaching out to her, demanding that she mustn't let go. All she wanted was for him to die. To just let it go and die.

'You don't understand, you can't understand …,' she cried. But she was exhausted and couldn't carry on. She couldn't keep this anger up any longer. For there seemed nothing more obvious, now, than that this man understood as much as anyone what it meant to have everything stolen away from him. A theft felt as keenly as her own. And in these moments of death he was sharing the last of his life with her. With her whom all had ignored for so many years. Sharing his final moments of life with someone who wanted him dead. Somehow, she felt like she was dying too. It was dark. She was on her knees, still bleeding, still unhealed. In front of her, a man was dying on a cross. Perhaps just another madman bleeding to death. But together they bled, through wounds that would never heal. This was their meeting, and as this man quietly fell dead, she sensed that in her bleeding he might always be with her.

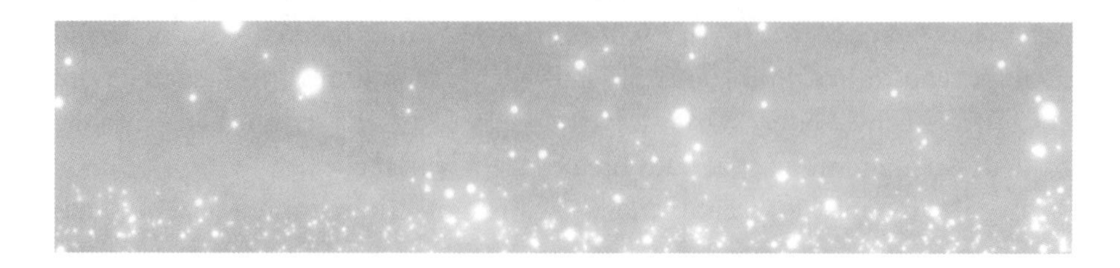

GOOD FRIDAY IN A NORTHERN TOWN[3]

God wasn't sure how she'd got into this position. To be sat on a rat-eaten armchair in a back alley used for dumping rubbish was not a place anyone wanted to be, whether you're God or not. But, somehow, it seemed right. The only place she could be today. One thing she knew for certain: she'd wet herself. Cold and damp against the pain of her legs. Pain in her everywhere. She wanted to wipe the mess and snot off her face and tried to raise her hand and head to meet each other. It was too much and she let them fall. So she just sat there – a flabby bulk, prematurely aged, in a stained, too-old sack that might once have been a dress, and decayed sandals that were just the worst thing for this time of year. She tried to shout, but made hardly any sound and what sound there was made no sense. It was near the end.

Beyond the bin bags and boxes the world carried on. She could still hear it – its busy self-concern echoed even here, but it was too afraid to come in. This was the place for its rubbish, rank and dark, for the things it didn't want. Couldn't stand to look at. Where else was there for her to be? She remembered the look from that girl in the chicken shop yesterday – the look of one who cares, who knows you shouldn't judge, but who's paralysed with disgust and fear. The others were just being abusive, filled with contempt, saying she smelled; but that one had wanted to act, to … and God had wanted to reach out and free her, but the time for action had passed. For the light of the world had already gone out and the world would have to have its say.

It was the singing of birds she wanted most. She could have died for a blackbird's song, for just one of her children to take up the hymns she'd taught them at the world's birth. Instead, there was nothing but the city's

---

[3] First published in Ruth Burgess & Chris Polhill eds., *Eggs & Ashes* (Glasgow: Wild Goose 2004).

vague industrial noise to counterpoint her lungs' labouring towards death. And the pigeon. The pigeon. God knows how long he'd been perched there. Which God found quite funny considering that she was God and she didn't know. But it hurt too much to laugh. The pigeon squatted uncomfortably on a melted wheelie bin, not wanting to get too close. He knew, you see, he'd worked out whom he was with. And he didn't like it one bit. For here, in the midst of the filth and crap, was God. Scummy and unloved. Here she was, down here with the likes of the pigeons, the vermin, the scum, and for better or worse it was as if she were one of them. It was too much for anyone to take in, let alone a pigeon, so he shuffled nervously to and fro, eyeing this God with the cautious look of one who's had to dodge an aimed kick once too often. God didn't seem to mind – she just sat, lungs grating, slowly dying, gently watching the pigeon and glad of a friend. They waited a while.

Darkness seemed to be coming on. The pigeon sensed rain, but knew this was no time to run. Today there was no shelter to be found. Here was his place, exposed, with his God – exposed and alone. Time was up. God knew it, the pigeon knew it. It was finished and God thought again of the girl in the mall, and the mocking voices and the gang of laughing drunken lads who'd beaten her to a pulp last night, and was so filled with love that she could do nothing but die.

The pigeon could hold out no longer, and with all the grace he could muster flapped his way into the open, dead hand of God. And, somehow, in the midst of the rotten, hopeless scene, in a place the world would rather forget, he knew that today he was with God in Paradise.

OVER THE RAINBOW

It wasn't Mrs Driscoll's thing – lounging in the street getting stoned until late into the night. Her idea of chilling out was going to Mass or eating scones with the Father at teatime, like someone out of a Sunday night TV snoozathon. A woman so pious she had religious tat in every corner of her house (down to the crucifix outside the front door). And she was a Class A hypocrite to boot: she'd go on about how such and such was a whore because she'd got pregnant at thirteen, but she wasn't really married herself. Everyone knew that 'Mr Driscoll' was her dance instructor who popped by for a quick one whenever he got bored.

Then there was her attitude to her son Stephen, a teenager for whom 'one-man crimewave' was total understatement. He'd graduated from pram to twoccing with no discernible intermediate steps and his gang oozed the casual threat of violence. But to Mrs Driscoll he was always her 'little Stephen', always the victim of others stronger than himself. No one could grasp her readiness to forgive or her hope that he'd repent from crime. And always the double standard – cheap and easy forgiveness for Stephen, condemnation for anyone else.

The day it happened, that final Sunday, most of us had been in the street since first sun, getting completely blitzed. Mrs Driscoll had attended Mass and disappeared behind her net-curtain wall. Stephen and his mates had been seen occasionally, kicking a football around. After that, they had disappeared for the rest of the afternoon. I smoked and dozed until evening, waking to the strains of 'Over the Rainbow', that modern version by the dead American woman. Most of the estate had retreated to wolf down their teas in front of repeats of home-counties' detective shows. The sun cast dappled shadows on our terraced box homes. Sirens made wild music as they bounced off houses in the distance. I went indoors and ate pizza.

It was past eleven when I wandered outside to be met by the stench of paint. The first shift at the chemical works, I thought. I breathed deep, seeking a cheap hit, though my reverie was cut short by a police car pulling up outside Mrs Driscoll's. No surprise there. But tonight was different. It was the way the WPC got out – more like a doctor carrying bad news than a copper. She hesitated before knocking. Upon answering the door, Mrs Driscoll started shouting, but the male officer cut her short. He mumbled something and, amazingly, she let them in without further complaint. Wanting to make sure Mrs Driscoll was all right, I got a kitchen chair and sat out front. But there was no helping her that night. For soon the officers reappeared herding Mrs Driscoll to the car like some fat, broken beast of burden being taken to the knacker's yard. It was obvious what news would have left her like that. I went inside and that was that for Sunday night.

Stephen Driscoll died that night. The verdict: asphyxiation while under the influence of narcotics. Stephen's gang had scored some quality smack. They bust into a boarded-up house and went upstairs. Stephen injected himself even though everyone said he hated needles. He overdosed, but that wasn't what killed him. It was smoke inhalation. The investigators said that someone must have dropped a lit fag downstairs and some rubbish caught alight. That I understand. What I don't get is why his mates abandoned him. Okay, maybe they panicked, but apparently they didn't even try to move him. They just fucked off like he'd dumped on them all their lives and got all he deserved. And I feel ashamed. Me, who'd tried to get stoned on the fumes blown across the estate – not from the paintworks, but from a dying house. A dying boy. It's said that when the firefighters found him, his clothes had melted into him, leaving his body as distorted as a cheap plastic doll thrown on an ebbing fire out of boredom or disgust.

The funeral was hugely attended. From the size of the crowd anyone would have thought he was one of those kids who die young of leukaemia rather than a smacked-up thug. Maybe we wanted to make sure he was dead. Or gloat over or pity stuck-up Mrs Driscoll. Perhaps we came to mourn.

Maybe not for Stephen so much as our failure to care as a community. After all, even Stephen had been a kid once. Mrs Driscoll asked for 'Over the Rainbow' to be played. She said she remembered hearing it the evening Stephen died and thought he'd have liked it at his funeral. Hardly. Still, the rainbow stuff gave Father Jones a biblical hook on which to hang Stephen's death and his mother's pain. Something about how in the Bible the rainbow is the sign of God's promise never to abandon us.

Nice story, but I wish God cared less about signs and more about action. Signs don't change anything. Then again I suppose Stephen's death was a sign to the estate that we needed to sort ourselves out. Which we've begun to do: we've got the council's attention now so maybe some regeneration money will come along. Which is no comfort to Mrs Driscoll. She's shattered, her life scooped out by loss and prescription medicines. She doesn't go to church any more and the religious tat is gone. She even told Father Jones to fuck off when he came round to see her. Fair enough. After all, what sign did Stephen's death offer to her? Surely that God had reneged on his promise and abandoned her.

There is one thing though. That plaster crucifix Mrs Driscoll had – the one attached to the wall by her front door. It was the first thing to be slung out, but in a way she's never got rid of it. For even now the crucifix leaves a telltale mark, a scar, of where it was. Like one of those shadows left by an atomic bomb blast. Maybe signs add up to nothing in the end, but it's tempting to believe this empty, ghostly cross, this discoloured brickwork, is a sign that a thrown-away God is still with his thrown-away Mrs Driscoll. There is no gold at the end of the rainbow, and most people's dreams don't come true, but on this estate I'd rather take my chances with a rainbow that's really a scarred and shadowed cross. One day, I hope Mrs Driscoll can feel this way too.

ANOTHER CROWN OF THORNS

I don't expect you to understand. I don't expect excuses. I expect what we always get – judgement … because that's the easy thing to do. It's easy to say they've just gone bad. Their moral compass has gone haywire. They've forgotten how to be good.

I have a family too. I care about stuff. I give to charity. I have standing orders, for God's sake. I did a fun run for a kiddies' hospice. When I'm home I like to take my dog for a walk. I love my wife and kids. I'd do anything for them.

You weren't there. You can't understand.

We'd been sent away to a fly-infested dump. We'd been told it was for glory or for peace or to make the world a better, safer place. The usual crap. And, no, we didn't believe it, but we went anyway. Because that's what you do when you're a soldier. You're under orders and you place yourself in danger because that's your job. And you don't want to let down your mates and you don't want to be left out. So you go and you stand shoulder to shoulder with them.

You can't imagine how hard the job is. Thousands of miles from home, worrying about your family – about what your wife might be getting up to when the boredom sets in, about how your kids are getting on at school. Missing your son's birthday … again. And the locals don't want you around. They hate you and can barely disguise it. And you give out stuff telling them they're free now and how we've come to help them.

And then one of your mates gets blown up. And another one. And the whole place is falling apart. And you see it – even in the little kids' eyes, kids no older than your own – you see the fear and the contempt and the loathing. And how they'll do almost anything to get you out.

And I understand that. No one wants strangers in their land. But can't they see we're just trying to make things better? That we want to help them and build them stuff. I mean some of the things these people believe are from the dark ages. Surely they want the terrorists and rebels and trouble-makers out of the way as much as we do?

And so it goes on. And you're scared and you're homesick and your mates keep dying or getting maimed. Have you even seen what happens when a young, fit man loses his legs or hands?

And this pressure builds in your head. And you want to lash out.

And then you capture one of the bastards … and don't give me this crap about innocent till proven guilty … there's no time for that here. And if a bloke is found hanging out with dodgy characters, what are you expected to think? Guilty by association.

Don't you get it? You've been working eighteen hours a day for months without a break. You're on constant alert. Your mates are getting attacked, maimed and killed and you haven't had a moment's love for forever. And you take the hood off one of these scum and they look at you with pleading eyes.

They look at you as if you might save them or free them. They cry like a child, like your own child might. And you can't stand it any more. And you have to lash out. You have to make them pay for what has been done. You'd happily nail them up yourself.

STONES

This was getting ridiculous, she thought. How difficult can it be to open your front door and step out? Yet this was how it had become – standing here day after day, morning after morning, knowing it was no good staying indoors. Knowing that she had a life to lead. Knowing that in some ways her whole future depended on stepping out into the world and facing it, whatever it might hold. How easy would it be to stay in? To come up with some excuse to hide. To say, well, just today … today I'll stay in, watch TV, call in sick … tomorrow I'll get back to it. Too easy, she thought.

She stood there a few moments longer, breathing as slowly and as evenly as she could, trying to look natural and relaxed, telling herself that whatever lay out there this morning, it could not define her. That they would not hold her back. That they were just being ignorant and foolish. That she was ok, that she looked ok, that she was not a freak. She took one final deep breath, fixed a smile on her face and stepped out into the August morning sun.

She got twenty yards before it started.

'Are you a boy or a girl?'

'A girl of course,' she replied, looking at the little girl, suddenly conscious of the nervous edge in her voice. Of how the nerves seemed to make her voice sound both gruffer and squeakier – like a man trying to sound like a woman. Her shoes suddenly seemed tighter, the make-up on her face a ridiculous mask.

'Dad called you a tranny …' replied the girl artlessly. She could have been no older than seven, the woman decided.

'That's not very nice,' she answered mildly, dying a little inside. Fighting back the tears. She couldn't blame the girl. She couldn't blame any of the kids really. She was bright enough to know that their meanness and mockery was not innate. It came from their scared, suspicious parents.

It had been going on for months – the stares, the mocking smiles, the men in particular looking at her with a strange mix of curiosity and fear. Attraction even. All of it wrapped up in an undercurrent of violent threat. And name-calling, of course. But it had taken a step up since the start of the summer holidays, with the kids out pretty much from dawn till dusk on sunny days. The name-calling had got vile. At first she'd tried talking to them, but that only seemed to make it worse. So she tried to ignore them or smile, walking the gauntlet with assured cool. It was exhausting.

She wished she'd never moved to this estate, but it was pretty much the only place she could afford. She'd also started wishing – to her annoyance – that she wasn't who she was. That she could be other. That God or nature, or whatever had made her this thing, had just made her a girl from the start. Or had helped her accept the gender she'd been given at birth. She hated herself for these thoughts because she'd told herself – post-transition – she'd never put herself down again. There were too many people out there who'd do that for free.

As she walked she looked down at her hands – her small, pale hands, her best feature she thought – not too big or too manly. Pretty hands. And she looked at the welts and the cuts on them and she could have wept. It wasn't just her hands. Her body felt sore from the stones they'd thrown at her the day before.

Just as she'd been skirting the park, a shower of stones had hit her and the shout of *freak* had come from a dozen or more children's voices. That had really shaken her up. She'd run home and sat for hours by the phone, picking up the receiver and putting it down again, trying to decide whether to call the police. But she didn't. What would the police do? Why should they care about people like her? They'd just take her details, tell her this was a serious crime and then snigger behind her back. And, anyway, who were they going to take it up with? A bunch of kids? The last thing she wanted was for these kids – kids already facing a hard time – to have more police on them. But she knew she was close to cracking, close to blowing up, close to lashing out.

She'd been so caught up in her thoughts, she'd forgotten the little girl. She hadn't noticed the girl tugging on her arm for attention.

'Miss … that's what *I* said …'

'What? Sorry?'

'I said it wasn't very nice … calling you a tranny …'

The woman stopped walking and stared at this little girl, seeing her properly for the first time. She was scrawny, with long brown hair and very pale skin. Her dress was a bit too big for her and had a frayed hem. There were bags under her eyes. Like so many kids on this estate, she did not look very well cared for. There was something almost funny about the way she jutted her jaw out and pulled herself up straight as she spoke, as if she had to fight to be heard. She probably always had.

The girl spoke again, asking, 'Is it hard?'

'How do you mean?' the woman replied, slightly bewildered by the way this conversation was heading.

'Being you,' the girl said.

The woman could have cried then. She wanted to say something grand or dramatic like, 'No harder than being you,' but all she could manage was, 'Yes …'

The girl nodded in the wise way only little children can manage.

The woman felt awkward as she noticed the girl looking at her bruised hands. To cover the silence, the woman said breezily, 'It's quiet today. Where is everyone?'

'I told them to leave you alone … I told them …' Her chin jutted out again as she spoke.

The woman felt her jaw drop. As she tried to pull herself together, she managed, 'Why did you do that?'

But the girl was already running off and the woman couldn't make out what she said.

The woman thought then about what a religious friend had said to her a few weeks before – about how her choice to take the risk of coming out and being faithful to herself was an act of resurrection. About how it was part of God's new creation. She'd struggled to believe that, just as much as she struggled to believe in any sort of god, other than one who laughed at the world.

She struggled to believe it still. But maybe just now she'd seen a glimpse in the kindness and bravery of a little girl. Because all she'd ever wanted since she'd stepped out the door for the first time as a woman was to be hidden, to blend in and to fit in. And now she'd been seen as if for the first time, and instead of it being horrible, it was good. She had been seen and it was good. And, for the first time in God knows how long, there was hope in the tears streaming down her face.

ANOTHER SUNDAY MORNING

A clammy handshake with the greeter, a mumbled good morning and a pew all to oneself – ahh, there's nothing quite like a Sunday celebration of Mass. Although I suspect that the last time most of our congregation celebrated anything was Coronation Day. Consider Mary Hawsfield. Ninety and never married, Mary never fails to deflate an audience with tales of her fifty glorious years as the church's youth work fuehrer; tales about how, in her day, the Sunday school was full, about how a sharp slap is the only language a small child understands. Or Kathleen Harper. Still formidable at seventy, Kathleen was voted 'Person most likely to publicly trample on the feelings of others' in last year's 'Church Personality of the Year' awards. Or would have been if the church held such awards. Kathleen is that most enduring feature of church life: the person who, whenever anyone suggests trying something new, pipes up with 'We've tried that before and it didn't work.' She says it so automatically I've considered suggesting the PCC have an orgy just to see if she trots out her overworked line.

So we wait for Fr Richard, our priest, to lead us in hymns of thanks and praise. All twenty of us, in a building that can take one hundred and fifty. Are the others are as dissatisfied as I am? Like Alice the pianist, practising an unintentionally funny song, or the two Darrens tuning their 'kumbayah' guitars. Or Big Ron, whose wooden leg, acquired during the Korean War, is easily his most animated part. Or anyone else for that matter, from old dotty Doris and her 'tea cosy' hat through to Bob Donahue (aka Glen Le Frondré, multi-quiffed club singer), our resident fundamentalist. Finally, Richard appears, bustling his way down the chancel as if anxious to get to another, more pressing, engagement. Which pretty much sums him up. An easy-to-like guy who is a slave to the jumble of appointments he commits himself to and whose true god is his diary. And, like most gods, his diary sets demands he simply cannot keep, leading to that hallmark of truly 'religious' behaviour – guilt. Guilt, followed by penitence, new resolve and a repeated and inevitable fall.

Fr Richard picks up his service sheet and says, 'Welcome! The Lord be with you!' Our mumbled response is met by an unexpected noise: the nave door creaking open. I turn and see a thin young woman enter. She's at once both nondescript – her clothes are plain and shabby, a stained white top and navy trousers – and, yet, remarkable. Her fragile frame somehow amplifies the intensity of her presence, especially her eyes – eyes which pop out of her shaved head, the blue irises against pinned retinas. Junkie eyes. She settles in an empty pew two rows behind me, and Di, one of the side persons, gingerly places an order of service next to her, smiling, trying to conceal her fear.

'We begin by singing our first hymn …' All any of us muster is a vague whisper that creeps out of our mouths, makes for heaven and, thinking better of the attempt, allows itself to be absorbed by silence. Although our pianist seems to be giving it her all as she practically reaches orgasm over a theologically dubious late-'70s love dirge to Jesus. And our shaven-headed friend seems to be having a good time – ignoring the song and mumbling excitedly to herself. And so the service drags on in its usual embarrassing way – a half-hearted attempt at Confession, an unconvincing Gloria and another stodgy hymn. And Ron, the lay assistant, doing his usual shocking attempt at reading the Gospel. A man whose reading skills are so limited his lips move when he looks at pictures. Until we come to the only tolerable part of the service – the sermon. For the sermon represents ten minutes when I can do whatever I want – snooze, play on my phone, press tacks into my forehead to keep myself awake. And being part of a small church in a big building has its advantages: you can have a pew to yourself, set up home, install a fridge and mini-bar. Make the hell around you just a bit more acceptable.

Today's sermon seems to be an attempt to put a psychological spin on the meaning of salvation and it becomes clear from the moment that Fr Richard begins talking about our 'inner tablecloth' (which we use to 'cover' a multitude of sins and make ourselves 'presentable' to others) that he's quickly skimmed through some Christian psychobabble and hasn't had time to prepare properly. He rambles and there are too many pauses. I start to lose interest, but as I do so, something unexpected happens.

'Shit!' It's our babbling guest, her voice full of venom. 'Shit! Complete fucking shit!' Her second outburst is enough to attract everyone's attention. We turn and gawp at her long, passionate face, all of us startled, a little excited and, in my case at least, mildly amused by her interruption. We wait, greedily, for her next comment; however, it is Fr Richard who speaks next: 'Is there a problem?'

'It's shit. It's all shit!' replies the woman. She's consistent, at least. This could become very tiresome. And then she shouts, 'What do you think you're doing?'

For the first time I realise she has a cultured voice. She says again, 'What do you think you're doing?' She's quieter this time and no one interrupts. She's got her platform, and intuitively we've realised it's better to let her speak, to let her burn herself out.

'Look at you all. As dismal as this fucking church. No wonder no one comes … no wonder no one wants to come … You couldn't persuade anyone to believe in God in a million years … church fucking mice … and do you know the worst of it? There's nothing here – no life, no nothing. You're all fucking dead already.'

There's a beat of silence and she's off, making for the door. As she reaches it, Kathleen Harper, who's sat halfway up the nave, stands and bellows, 'Just hold on a minute,' in a voice as cheap and unpleasant as a tabloid exposé. This brings an immediate pleading, 'Kathleen, please!' from Richard, but it's too late.

'Who do you think you are?'

Our accuser, now the accused, doesn't seem to hear. She's opening the door.

'You. Who do you think you are? Coming here, insulting us, not knowing us. Who do you think you are?'

Slowly, the woman turns and, evenly, looks Kathleen dead in the eye. Then, in a measured voice, says, 'Who am I? I would have thought that was obvious.'

Her eyes fall from Kathleen's, and become opaque with her own thoughts. She opens the door and goes, leaving her last remark hanging in the air like incense. Leaving us feeling confused and embarrassed. No, more than that – ashamed. Well, that's what I feel. I don't know why. After all, she's obviously just another local loony, probably booted out 'into the community' when the big hospital shut a few years back. Kathleen is clearly unaffected. She shrugs and sits, as if the incident is already dismissed, no doubt because our visitor's opinion is – as far as she can see – merely mad. I'm not so sure. And when Richard speaks, his train of thought stumbling, it becomes clear that I'm not alone:

'I feel that … after all that excitement (a little nervous laughter from the congregation) perhaps we should press on a little … my sermon wasn't that good anyway. (More laughter – more confident this time.) So we come to our time of prayer.'

To be honest, I pay no attention to the rest of the service, a symptom of the effect our visitor has had on me – of how she's mainlined into all that I feel about this place. She might be bonkers, but she's seen as clearly as anyone can that what we do here on a Sunday is as moving and potent as a Mills and Boon novel. She knows as well as I do that we've forgotten how to worship. Perhaps even how to recognise God. That our attendance here is inexplicable, unless we are caught up in some sort of unshakeable habit – a ritual of the already dead. A compulsion as hard and useless as smoking cigarettes.

Yet, perversely, I'm excited. I feel like you do at 3am sometimes, when you're convinced you've had the world's greatest idea. And I'm thinking, maybe this time I'm going to break the habit of this place and take up something more useful, like DIY. But, even as I think that, it already seems dishonest. There's more to my excitement than that. I feel a wave of hope beginning to churn, like water snapping and foaming way out in a bay, slowly building and gathering into a breaker. I feel like I'm a child again, going away on holiday, spotting the sea and feeling that surge of hope after endless 'Are we there yets?' For I sense forming in my imagination a new image of what our church might be. An image as bright and fresh as my childhood dreams about how magical my summer holiday was going to be, as startling and real as the cold Atlantic surf that each year washed them away.

Our junkie friend has clearly 'got' to me. Such was her passion, it was as if she were speaking out for God, or God was speaking through her. And what she was saying was that what we do in church, in this church at least, isn't just shit and lifeless, it crucifies God. But I want to say more than that. What I want to say is that if, in some sense, what we do here crucifies God, we are being crucified with her. That's what really excites me: We are the crucified too. Although I'm not sure how that can be exciting, or even what I mean when I say that. Or why I say it.

Perhaps all I want to say is that if we have a place with God, it is alongside her in her torment. That even as she is pushed out of the world, we must be willing to go – we have to go – over the edge with her. As if that's the only kind of 'church' that makes sense in a place like this. And that such a church is very close to God. In fact, it's the only way we in this church can be close to God. After all, we're not the efficient or the wise or the holy. I'm not even sure we're much of a community either. I mean, Mary Hawsfield has barely spoken to 'dotty' Doris for fifteen years because of some petty dispute over who was in charge of running a jumble sale. And Fr Richard's diary is so full I don't think he ever has the time to help us become closer. Come to think of it, I'm not sure I'd want to get very close to most of the people who come here, or they to me.

But we come week after week, mostly wrapped up in ourselves, occasionally intersecting, even talking to each other (and usually recoiling). And all most of us have is our need, our illnesses and fears. Our sense that we're near the edge of the world and, maybe, we're about to go over. Because that's what life is like on an estate like this – with few exceptions, a meeting of the damaged and tired. And, in the case of Dave and his partner Janice, the smelly. But they have a place here and their messy story of illness and poverty and tragedy (their three-year-old granddaughter died of leukaemia earlier this year) is simply a striking variation on most of the congregation's experience. Mary Hawsfield, for all her bluff, cannot hide her anxiety, nigh on panic, about her failing senses and rapidly dimming mind. I reckon most of the older people (which is most of the congregation) feel like that. They're not really that worried about death, only about losing the things that make them themselves. Even Kathleen, tough old Kathleen Harper, cannot conceal her loneliness and unresolved loss at her husband's death. And Bob Donahue, who so fervently believes in the grace of God touching him, whose joy in the Lord is a wonder to behold, is marked by shadow behind the sunshine. Because Bob's terrified about his recent diagnosis of cancer and prayer hasn't healed him yet. So the story goes on, across almost everyone in the congregation – pain and exhaustion rarely mentioned, but real nonetheless.

And I'm no different. For all my cynicism and posturing, I'm a mess. Because, after years of illness, an endless up-hill that feels like decline, I've forgotten how to be myself and be myself well. My best remaining skill is trying to hide my self-pity by mocking others. But still I come. Each week we all come, mostly to sit and listen or drift off or do nothing. Or ignore other people. And probably why we attend is not entirely clear to most of us. Being here is enough. Perhaps because we are welcome. Smelly or poor or depressed, we're welcome. Even as we sense ourselves being pushed, like God, out of the world, we're welcome. Precisely because we're not some super-energised elect of God, but because we're ourselves; tired, bust-up, fucked-up, muddled and in need. And I'm sure that's pretty much what God's like too – at least round these parts. And I hope she feels welcome in this church. I hope she'll feel welcome again.

THE GARDEN OF TEARS*

It had been the worst summer in living memory. The storms had raged for weeks, washing out carnivals and parades, cricket matches and summer dreams. Every day, the news had been full of stories of misery and flood; of pundits claiming it was driving businesses to the wall and modern-day Jeremiahs predicting it was only going to get worse as the planet heated up.

But today was different. Today was sunshine and laughter and joy. Today everyone wanted to be outdoors and the park was full. Parents seemed just as happy as their kids for once, tirelessly playing games with their toddlers, running after footballs, and rejoicing in the sun. Old friends and new settled down for a day of fun, of games and relaxation. Old and young lazed and all was right with the world. Even the teenage tribes – the skate kids, the fashion freaks, the metalheads and the Goths – weren't bickering for once. Everyone was just happy to be outdoors. Nobody seemed to mind having the mick taken out of them for wearing all black on a blazing hot day. No one seemed to mind being ribbed for being a fashion victim, paying stupid money for a pair of trendy trainers made in a sweatshop. It was that kind of day. And most of the teenagers knew each other anyway. They'd grown up together. They might act as if they weren't friends half the time, but they were all children of the same place. The same town. And it was good to have a Saturday when everyone could get out and chat and catch some sun.

God was very glad too. Glad to get out and hang with her friends. Glad to be able to chat about music and future plans and who was hot and who was not. It was great to just get outdoors and not be worried for once about the way the world seemed to be heading. It was great to slap some serious make-up on and get her favourite *Cradle of Filth* t-shirt on show. She knew it wasn't always easy for the people of her world to get on and she knew that even as she and her friends were relaxing there were others in the world in great suffering and distress. And she wished it wasn't so and she tried to help people be better and kinder and share the abundance of riches the world has. But today, for once, she'd relax, enjoy the beauty of the trees and the cool of the grass as if it were Eden and not just a park in an unknown town. Sure, it wasn't exactly cool for a Goth to be seen enjoying the sun too much, but for once she thought: What the hell? You can have too much gloom and black.

So God sat out in the park all day, listening to tunes, watching the people relax until the shadows lengthened and almost everyone had gone home. It was twilight, her favourite time, when the world was balanced between day and night, when people were preparing to settle after a long day. She went and sat on the big swings and rocked back and forth, feeling the very last rays of the red sun tickle her neck. Even if the world was messed up, in this moment, she thought, everything was all right.

She didn't hear the gang of lads step up behind her. She was too absorbed in her dreams for the future, in enjoying the moment of oneness she felt. The first she knew were the words and the sneers. 'Now, lads, what have we got here? Is it a lad or a lass?' A reedy voice, only recently broken, God surmised, backed up by laughter, low and edgy, animal even, like hyenas braying.

And then she saw them, as they circled around. Eight of them, all lads she'd seen about town. All in their early teens. All falling in behind the boy who'd spoken, a smallish wiry lad with a mirthless grin on his face. God stared at him. She knew him. She didn't know his name, but she knew his face. More than that she knew the look on that face. She'd seen it on the faces of countless men.

'What a state to get yourself in, eh?' said the wiry boy, playing to his audience. There were murmurs of 'disgrace' amid the laughter. 'Like something out of a freak show. Bloody Goths.'

God tried not to smile to herself. The boys surrounding her were hardly the finest specimens of manhood she'd ever seen. Their clothes were cheap and ill-fitting. Their baseball caps seemed too huge for their heads. They stank of weed and cheap alcohol. A couple of them sucked on fags. Now, she decided, was not a time for jokes. She quickly looked around – trying to spot anyone she might know who hadn't gone home yet, anyone out walking the dog. No one. She tried to calculate how far she'd have to run if it came to it. Too far.

'So what do they call you? Franken-freak?' The boy tittered at his own joke. He'd edged in closer, God noticed. Very slowly she got up off the swing and stood to face him. She could see his surprise that she was taller than him. The advantage of a decent pair of boots. Casually she replied, 'You wouldn't believe me if I said …' She looked at him with her sad, heavily made-up eyes and began to walk off, praying that the rest of his gang would have enough sense not to push it. That they'd still be young enough to be worried about being caught doing something they'd all regret. That they'd remember she was a person. She tried to ignore the nagging doubt in her mind that crowds and gangs were different. That even good people could be carried away.

Before she got two yards, the boy had grabbed her around the wrist.

'Don't you walk away from me, bitch …' She could smell the cheap cider on his breath. She wanted to cry out with the pain, but she wouldn't give him the satisfaction. She stared at his bleary, frenzied eyes. She could see his fear, his bravado and his longing to be loved. She could see his loneliness. Behind him, half of the gang were cheering and egging him on. A couple were anxious, telling him to calm down and not be a dick. One lad – clearly the youngest – had gone very pale and looked terrified.

God could feel her heart beginning to race. She had to keep her mind clear. Because she could see from this boy's bloodshot eyes that his mind was a mess, that he was almost beyond reason. That he was so weak and insecure he felt he had to prove something. That he was so lacking in power he had to show his power in the nastiest way. She had one chance now. To get away and run and hope she'd find someone to help her.

With all her might she kneed him between his legs. He yelped with shock, doubled over and let go. And God ran … She ran like she had when the world was young, before all its innocence had been lost. And she thought of what redemption might look like in this cruel world and if there were things that might be unforgivable. And she ran, her lungs burning, as she heard the fury of the hounds behind her.

And then she was falling, her head suddenly cloudy, pain burning at the back. She fell onto the grass, at the edge of a copse of trees, and tried to push herself up. As she did so, she saw a bloody stone and understood the cause of her fall. She touched the damp at the back of her head and looked at her bloody hand.

She saw the gang close in on her, panting, some of them spitting up phlegm from the run. She saw their angry eyes and heard their vile curses. She saw the nasty eyes of the lad she'd kicked and thought how little this gang resembled the creatures she'd made a thousand ages ago. These were not humans but animals. And the lad was going on about how he was going to teach her a lesson, as he began to undo his belt.

God prayed then. She looked at the terrified youngest boy, her eyes imploring. She looked for an ally in the crowd, but there didn't seem to be one. They had lost themselves in a mob. She told herself, *I will not be their victim* … but how could she not be now? She prayed there was some way to fight back with love and not hate, now there was no escape. She saw the terrified young man, barely more than a child, run off.

And it was night.

*For Sophie Lancaster and all who dare to be different.

THE MISUNDERSTANDING

God had had to get used to misunderstanding. After all, from the beginning, they'd been getting him wrong. He'd made the world in love and for love but they didn't want to get it. It was infuriating. The insects got it. The fish and the birds and sloths and the bison got it. But his precious ones, the ones who bore his very image, just could not. They'd use any opportunity to blame him for their spectacularly bad choices. And – he had to admit – he couldn't avoid all responsibility. He had given them free will. And he had not regretted it for one moment.

However, things had gotten really out of hand when it came to rules. God understood that people wanted guidance. He understood that without rules selfish humanity was lost. But they had such a gift for seeing problems where there were none. They loved to make regulations for themselves. And they felt better when they could claim those rules all came from God.

But it was covenant he longed for, not regulation – relationship not rules. All he wanted was for the peoples of the earth to be in right relationship with him and with each other. He wanted them to know that he was for them. That at the heart of all things was love – sacrificial love, and passionate love, and friendship. If they wanted to try to live without him he wouldn't stop them, but his heart broke when he saw how unhappy their fights and battles and wars made them.

So he let them build walls and make unnecessary rules. He let them have kings to rule them and imagine that all they did – their violence and love of power – was really being done for the sake of God. He sensed their sacrifices and the fear that was contained within them. He wept when he saw how they thought their sacrifices were appeasing his anger and wrath. And he sent to them guides and wise men and women to show them the way home. But they loved the dead end. Some would listen and some would not, and too often the people chose the easy path – the path which did not welcome the stranger or honour the poor; the path which reserved the image of God for the powerful and comfortable or for anyone who loved to honour themselves; the path which treated anything different as threatening and unholy. And from time to time the people saw where God's messengers were pointing them and understood and moved on a bit. But in the end there was no one to go but himself.

When he'd arrived in the city, a parade – a carnival, a Festival of Lights – was going on. This was more like it, he thought. How often had his people made life a misery? How often had they imagined that what mattered was piety and seriousness and fear? But at this parade was all of life – young and old, male and female and more besides, all cultures, all ethnicities. This was a rainbow people dancing and singing. *This is the way to enter a city*, he thought and he fell in with the crowd and danced and sang.

Yet when he saw the angry faces at the edge of the crowd he could have wept. He'd rarely seen a sadder sight than the little group of protesters, shouting with placards, screaming that this festival was a sin and unholy. Then, further back, in the shadows, another group, more sinister, a scowling gang looking silently on at the parade, disgust on their faces. God understood what they were about only too well – they just couldn't stand anyone who wasn't like them. They were terrified about what lay within them and he prayed for them, for their liberation, because they'd made prisons for themselves.

But there was nothing he could do for them this day. They were not there to listen or be changed. That would have to wait for another day, another year. So he partied and danced and rejoiced in this feast and gave himself to the song. Till finally he was dancing and talking and laughing with a small group of celebrating folk and they partied into the small hours. And though they invited him to carry the party on through the night, God was happy and had had enough. He wanted to be alone. To wander off on this warm, glorious night and be glad. To get out of the city and look at the stars and dream. So he wandered away from the energy and the lights, barely able to conceal his grin of delight, till slowly the crowds thinned and he was alone.

That was when he sensed them, drawing closer in the night. He began to walk faster, thinking he could throw them off. He knew exactly who they were. They were that gang who'd lurked in the shadows. Or people very much like them. Angry people. Frightened people. As he thought about it, a new determination filled him. That instead of running, he would face them. He would talk. Because buried in them, however faintly, was his image too. He would make them listen. Because he was no mere messenger or prophet – he was God.

So he slowed and felt their fear and malice and anger draw near, till there was a gang of them surrounding him, glowering, their fear fierce as a blaze. And he smiled modestly at them as they taunted him and called him the vilest names. They mocked his clothes and the way he looked. They used the worst names for gay men they could imagine. And he wept as he saw how lost his taunters were. He wept for all the good people they'd hurt. He tried to absorb all their hate and take all the things he said into his embrace. And then he tried to speak.

But they would not let him.

THE LOST

Home had always been where the hatred was. That's why I ran away as soon as I could. When I left seven years ago I breathed for the first time. After all, I was not 'of them'; did not want to be 'of them'. Most of all I did not want to be thought of as 'of him'. My father's soul was made of money; mostly notes of low denomination that he covered up with large ones to impress his friends. But that was not what made him so horrible. It was the other things that he did to me. And to my brother. And to my mum. Though I cannot think of either of them with love. Because they sought to make the best of it. Especially mum. She wanted to explain away all that had been done. She loved to make things seem right and good. She cared for how it all appeared to the world. She wanted to live in the glow of the glory of my father, the popular and powerful man.

So I ran and ran, barely fifteen, till I came to the city. Four hundred miles away and drunk on petrol and neon light and the roar of the lost. And I saw my family's pleas on TV, for father was an influential man, and I saw my face appearing on milk bottles and on noticeboards in shops. But those who sought me – the police, the social services, even my family – didn't know I'd long since been swallowed up by the lost. And I was determined not to be found. I was already trying to change who I was, to get away from him, my father, and my mum too. Changing how I looked and acted in the hope of throwing off all that they had given me.

I will not say what I did to survive. Only that men – always men – are capable of awful things. But I knew what I wanted and who I needed to become, or so I thought. And I set about it. And I survived. I tried to remake my life and I saved and I found my own way, and with the help of the friends I found I became something new. Not the boy my parents had used and abused, but a woman. And I will not lie. Every single moment was tough, and changing my body and my look and who I was didn't take away the pain or what had been done to me, either by my family or by those I took money from. But in my emptiness I began to find a way ahead. And I found a way out of selling myself and I survived and made a home of sorts and a life that was for more than just escaping the past.

But perhaps there is no escape for people like me. The more I sought to let the past go, the better I got at forgetting, the more I saw it in everything. I saw my father's face on those of strangers. I'd sometimes not know if I was awake or dreaming, the nightmares became so real. I could not force the pictures away. There were drugs, of course. And therapists. And friends saying I should call the police, though I could never see why they'd believe me. All of it led one way, as far as I could see, the way I didn't want to go – back to the source, back to face them down. So, in the end, I put on the best dress I owned and took the next train out of town.

When I arrived, the walk from the station was like stepping into a photograph of the past – the park, the shops, the houses seemed fixed in time. And all the while the pressure of what I had to do was building in my head, bubbling like a photograph held over a flame. I'd made a mistake. What reason had I even to think that my parents were still alive or, if they were, that they lived in that monstrous house? And why would they see me anyway? Except to gloat or deny or turn away.

And then I saw him – father – fatter than ever. Those large, horrible hands. Walking towards me. I froze, wanting to run, but it was like my body had broken. I stood there, a manikin, jaw gaping. As he walked, he glanced across at me, appraising me. I have seen that look a thousand times on men's faces, the look of men who know they're safe and know that there is nothing you can do to fight back. And then he smiled and was past me and gone. I turned and saw him look back, nod his head, and walk on. If I had had a knife I would have stabbed him then, I think. Except I could not move for shaking and the feeling I was going to be sick at any moment. And I felt like I'd already lost. He didn't even see me or recognise me.

I should have turned around then and gone, but I could not. My burning, blistered feet wouldn't stop. And I found that all the dignity I'd so neatly buttoned up earlier in the day was running down my face in tears. Secretly I'd imagined that coming back here would be a kind of victory. For years I'd imagined my return, how it would be my moment of triumph, of *Look at me, see what I have become, see I have become me*. And all I had was silence. It seemed like there was only one place left to go.

Every leaf seemed assaulted by gnats and midges and flies. Already the plums were splitting on the branch, damsons lay pecked fleshless by blackbird, sparrow and crow on the ground. The air was curling, bent over with the stink of bird shit and fruit and plants just too alive, too far gone. But this was my place. The place in the grounds of my family's house that I'd called my own. The place into which I crawled as a child when I wanted to feel less alone, when I wanted to feel alone. The place where I went to escape what my father had done to me. Where it wasn't wrong to be confused. Where my body couldn't be seen, even by a God. Where I prayed to whatever God there was to strike my father down and make it all go away. Here was the place I pretended to be other people, to be anything other than myself. Where I practised putting make-up on, where I studied my face for the appalling growth of manhood, where I smashed a mirror in disgust and held a shard over my penis, ready to chop it off. Only to lose my nerve; only to curl up in a ball and sob and sob and see no way out. Until I was empty and silent and staring. Here was the place I first planned my escape and kept the things I used to run off. Where I saw a dream of who I could be and promised myself that it would happen. Where I whispered and shouted and finally screamed the truth and the startled crows said amen as they cawed and flew. Where I first refused silence and planned my survival.

Here nothing had changed – the undergrowth was wilder, the cheap discarded pots of old make-up hummed with insects, but nothing had really changed. Pieces of mirror still lay here and there, reflecting brown nature on the edge of dying. And I picked up a piece, mossy edged, spotted with dirt and droppings, pointed like a spearhead and I looked at myself and saw for the first time that everything had changed. I saw the lines spreading from the corners of my eyes and the clump of nasty black hairs on my right cheek that no amount of electrolysis could remove. I saw the thin skin that my make-up shows up rather than hides and the blue eyes lined with dark pencil. But I saw also that there is no homecoming, only survival or death. And I am surviving. And if I stop now, the old world will win. And if there is to be new life I cannot let it win. Silence will not be enough. So I let the spearhead of glass fall, and began the long walk back to the house.

LAZARUS

Men and women rush   searching for bodies
rich in sweat and pain to heal
but I have no fear

I have known the dark   its cloying warmth
I have lain where steel is clean
where there are others   who close their eyes
who are silent and refuse to dream

I stand at the threshold   paths tapping with feet
faces looking in   looking out

I spark the match   suck the smoke   blink and breathe
taste a world made flesh

THE RISEN LIFE

You wake to a sting between the shoulder blades
as if someone's folded a crease down your back.
The silence hurts, and the light unexpected –
grey, not quite morning, glowing at the edges
as if electric is involved. So many people,
lying down, confined, each in their own bay,
the slow heave of chests, a faint scent (antiseptic perhaps?),
the calm.

Not remembering for a second what has happened to you,
then feeling out from the inside a kind of shock
shivering down through your forehead, teeth, neck,
a fear about what might have been removed.

There is a nurse, she could be a nurse, someone who smiles,
who is not afraid of wounds, whose eyes twinkle
as she holds a finger to her mouth
when you begin to speak.

HIGH DEPENDENCY

We are where
miracles hide in curtain folds
where breath is regulated

bodies drift and halt
work according to plans we do not understand
dispensing dreams

veins of red and black rise from our arms
plastic coils extending out and upwards searching
grace falling with the leisure of snow

AMONG THE DEAD

You get wise to their tricks –
the short-cons, pigeon drops,
the way they lay ridiculous bets.
Their pockets are empty, you see.

It is weight they crave,
the feel of coin, the bumps
and stains of use, how a wallet
can shape itself to a single hand.

Sometimes they speak
What day …? Have you seen …?
But they do not stay for long.
They dart and flow in shoals.

How they clap and roar
when fire is breathed, cheer
when a child falls.

GHOSTS

They dream of us, of course:
of sipping whisky in the bath,
steam streaming from their heads,
the ache of limbs after winter walks.
Searching for a way to climb back in.

You see them crowding
round sick beds, waiting
for their chance. How
they fight like angry dogs.

They do not understand,
they hold no means to reweave
the broken code, to make
the helix whole. The weight
too much for their hands.

Their cries as the glass slides
through their grip. The still-warm coat,
slung on the floor, refusing to lift.

DIVINE SERVICE, APRIL 9TH 1945

'This is the end –
for me the beginning' – *Bonhoeffer*

One last time they herd us
our flesh moon white
waiting for the cut

but we have come for news

and if today
it is too slick
for us to hold
jittery and quick
as a fish

there are words
which can move the bulk
of a man

there is bread
which thunders and roars

there is blood
thick and hot
which falls like rain
on dying land.

THE KISS

He was shaking that night too:
her lips fierce, the scent of musk
and pomegranates, jewels hanging
from her hands. The way her eyes
assessed him. How she took money,
pushed him away.

The first kiss he always said

He would pay all he had –
lay open veins, see what
currency flowed within –
to be taken in hand
back through narrow streets
to meat and wine and bitter herbs,
back to the old story, to light and fire
and generous arms. He watches himself go,
but no.

There is another kiss

HANDWASHING

Sometimes just a finger
stroked absently across
the surface, breaking it
with a nail, will do.
As long as it is there
six or seven times a day,
the bowl kept cool,
the rose petals
not allowed to sink.

Now he pushes his hands beneath,
wanting to touch the curve of clay.
Half expecting to come up against nothing,
imagining going deeper and deeper
in. Frightened by the thought.

He rubs his palms together, allowing
his fingers to mesh, wishing it was
so easy to make ideas knit,
pulls them apart,
studies the lines curving down
towards his wrists, understanding
nothing they have to say.

I could walk away.
I could be mercy.
There is nothing I could not do.

JOSEPH OF ARIMATHEA

How easy it would be to say
I gave what I gave for love;
to save his body from the dogs,
the endless dark of howls and bones
breaking, of meat found by doors,
swept away in the dawn.

But I was already travelling
back to where we began,
searching through the carcass
of the festal lamb for a scrap
of understanding; ravenous to know
how food for escaping bodies
might be a guide to an end
and a beginning.

I had become as empty
as a ghost, rootless as a seed.
So I gave him my own room
of want, thinking it might
ground us both, break our
endless fast, ripen ancient fruit.

EMMAUS

Find me when the journey ends and the sun
bleeds into night; and I shall conjure spelt's
wild thunder, make bread crack and roar,
tear stories with my hands, let grain shatter and fall.

And we shall eat in the dark, mute in wonder,
understanding or not; will walk softly in the fields
as if we still breathed, as if we knew the company
of the dead, our dreams trembling in the dawn.

And we shall speak as if our mouths
are no longer our own; I going on ahead,
if that is what you need, learning secret tongues,
searching melodies and chords for glorious song.

ASCENDING

To cast off weight, to hollow
out bones, to bend her
voice higher
reaching

she has strength enough for that

for pushing the feathers out
to force the unexpected notes
up through her throat

she is coming down
to what she has left

she is discovering sound –
coos and trills –
body as flute

nothing
will hold her long
she could rise
as easily as dust.

END

What we became, after salt
burned the snow away,
I don't know.

We saw only the beach receding,
groynes smudged out,
sea and sky blurring.

At the pier's end films played,
bright with other visions:
Icebergs melting, freezing,
locking lands, washing them away.
Bees forgetting how to dance, a desert
bleaching human bones.

On the sands a man
walked slowly into the grey.
Further out lightning sparks,
a furnace of flames.

Wild Goose Publications, the publishing house of the Iona Community established in the Celtic Christian tradition of Saint Columba, produces books, e-books, CDs and digital downloads on:

- holistic spirituality
- social justice
- political and peace issues
- healing
- innovative approaches to worship
- song in worship, including the work of the Wild Goose Resource Group
- material for meditation and reflection

For more information:

Wild Goose Publications
Fourth Floor, Savoy House
140 Sauchiehall Street,
Glasgow G2 3DH, UK

Tel. +44 (0)141 332 6292
Fax +44 (0)141 332 1090
e-mail: admin@ionabooks.com

or visit our website at
www.ionabooks.com
for details of all our products and online sales